GET READY FOR GRADE **3**

TEACHER RECOMMENDED

# Kids

# SUMMER

## ACADEMY

### ARGOPREP

**7 DAYS A WEEK**

# 12 WEEKS

- Mathematics
- English
- Science
- Reading
- Writing
- Experiments
- Mazes
- Puzzles
- Fitness

**GRADE 2-3**

ArgoPrep is one of the leading providers of supplemental educational products and services. We offer affordable and effective test prep solutions to educators, parents and students. Learning should be fun and easy! To access more resources visit us at www.argoprep.com.

Our goal is to make your life easier, so let us know how we can help you by e-mailing us at: info@argoprep.com.

# Want free worksheets?

Visit us at argoprep.com/worksheets

- ArgoPrep is a recipient of the prestigious **Mom's Choice Award**.
- ArgoPrep also received the 2019 **Seal of Approval** from Homeschool.com for our award-winning workbooks.
- ArgoPrep was awarded the 2019 **National Parenting Products Award**, **Gold Medal Parent's Choice Award** and **the Tillywig Brain Child Award**.

# TABLE OF CONTENTS

# TABLE OF CONTENTS

# TABLE OF CONTENTS

# TABLE OF CONTENTS

# HOW TO USE THE BOOK

Welcome to **Kids Summer Academy** by ArgoPrep.

This workbook is designed to prepare students over the summer to get ready for **Grade 3.** The curriculum has been divided into **twelve weeks** so students can complete this entire workbook over the summer.

Our workbook has been carefully designed and **crafted by licensed teachers** to give students an incredible learning experience.
Students start off the week with English activities followed by Math practice. Throughout the week, students have several fitness activities to complete. Making sure students stay active is just as important as practicing mathematics.
We introduce yoga and other basic fitness activities that any student can complete. Each week includes a science experiment which sparks creativity and allows students to visually understand the concepts. On the last day of each week, students will work on a fun puzzle.

# HOW TO WATCH VIDEO EXPLANATIONS
### IT IS ABSOLUTELY FREE

Go to **argoprep.com/summer3**
OR scan the QR Code:

# RECOMMENDED READING LIST

One of the best ways to increase your reading comprehension level is to read a book for at least **20** minutes a day. We strongly encourage students to read several books throughout the summer. Below you will find a recommended summer reading list that we have compiled for students entering into Grade 3 or simply visit us at: www.argoprep.com/**summerlist**

Author: Louis Sachar
Title: Marvin Redpost

Author: Megan McDonald
Title: Judy Moody

Author: Cynthia Rylant
Title: Henry and Mudge

Author: Barbara Robinson
Title: The Best School Year Ever

Author: E. B. White
Title: Charlotte's Web

Author: Mary Pope Osborne
Title: Summer of the Sea Serpent

Author: Liesl Shurtliff
Title: Jack: The True Story of Jack and the Beanstalk

Author: Katherine Applegate
Title: The One and Only Ivan

Author: Beverly Cleary
Title: The Mouse and the Motorcycle

Author: Patricia MacLachlan
Title: Sarah, Plain and Tall

# BOOKS BY ARGOPREP

Here are some other test prep workbooks by ArgoPrep you may be interested in. All of our workbooks come equipped with detailed video explanations to make your learning experience a breeze! Visit us at www.argoprep.com

## COMMON CORE MATH SERIES

## COMMON CORE ELA SERIES

    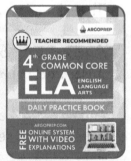

# INTRODUCING MATH!

Introducing Math! by ArgoPrep is an award-winning series created by certified teachers to provide students with high-quality practice problems. Our workbooks include topic overviews with instruction, practice questions, answer explanations along with digital access to video explanations. Practice in confidence - with ArgoPrep!

# SOCIAL STUDIES

Social Studies Daily Practice Workbook by ArgoPrep allows students to build foundational skills and review concepts. Our workbooks explore social studies topics in depth with ArgoPrep's 5 E's to build social studies mastery.

# KIDS SUMMER ACADEMY SERIES

ArgoPrep's **Kids Summer Academy** series helps prevent summer learning loss and gets students ready for their new school year by reinforcing core foundations in math, english and science. Our workbooks also introduce new concepts so students can get a head start and be on top of their game for the new school year!

## WATER FIRE

## DANCE HERO

## ADRASTOS THE SUPER WARRIOR

## MYSTICAL NINJA

## FIRESTORM WARRIOR

## RAPID NINJA

## CAPTAIN ARGO

## THUNDER WARRIOR

## CAPTAIN BRAVERY

## GREEN POISON

### Give your character a name
Cameron

Write down the special ability or powers your character has and how you will help your community with the powers.

She stops bad things from happening because she can see the future.

**Great!** You are all set. To become an incredible hero, we need to strengthen our skills in **english**, **math** and **science**. Let's get started.

# JANUARY
## WEEK 1

WINTER

Did you know January has 31 days? The month of January is named after the Roman god Janus. In North America, during the month of January, the season is winter.

Now that you're done with second grade, you should have the skills you need to become a much better reader and writer than you were just a few years ago when you were in kindergarten. You will be expected to read and write longer texts, which means you need to know how to **summarize**.

A **summary** is a quick explanation of what something longer (like a book, movie, or personal story) was about <u>**without**</u> communicating every single detail. Summaries are important for **saving time** and helping people focus on **main ideas**, rather than getting distracted by less important information. This week, you'll be thinking about creating summaries through a variety of activities.

## <u>Key Terms:</u>

Summary: A brief explanation of a text's main points or ideas
- It could be...
  - o A book
  - o A movie
  - o An episode of a TV show
  - o Something that happened in real life
  - o ...pretty much anything!

Summarize: To read something (like a book or article) and create a <u>summary</u> based on it.

## <u>Hints & Strategies for Creating a Summary:</u>

- Read or review the text you are summarizing **closely**
- Look for **main ideas**
  - o What does the author present at the beginning?
  - o What ideas get repeated?
- Focus on the information people **<u>need to know</u>**, not things that are nice to know.
- Don't include too much information
  - o Information overload defeats the whole purpose of creating a summary!

## <u>When Summarizing a Paragraph...</u>

- Look at what the author discusses in the <u>first</u> and <u>last</u> sentences
  - o These can be keys for recognizing main ideas
- Think about what vocabulary or terms the author is defining
  - o If the text is teaching you new words or ideas, those are probably the most important things in the text
- Ask yourself: "How would I explain this paragraph to someone in **<u>just one clear sentence?</u>**"

## From "Lad: a Dog"

### By Albert Payson Terhune

He slept in a "cave" under the piano. He even had access to the sacred dining-room, at mealtimes - where always he lay to the left of the Master's chair.

With the Master, he would willingly unbend for a romp at any or all times. At the Mistress' behest he would play with all the silly abandon of a puppy; rolling on the ground at her feet, making as though to seize and crush one of her little shoes in his mighty jaws; wriggling and waving his legs in air when she buried her hand in the masses of his chest-ruff; and otherwise messing around with complete loss of dignity.

But to all except these two, he was calmly unapproachable. From his earliest days he had never forgotten he was an aristocrat among inferiors.

1. **Underline** the part of the text that shows how Lad treated people who were not his owners.

2. What **hints** in the text tell you that the character being described is a **dog**?

He slept in a cave under the piano, rolling on the ground at her feet, his mighty jaws, and his chest-ruff.

3. Which of these is the best **summary** of the **second** paragraph?

   **A.** The dog in the story was very playful with his owners.
   **B.** The dog in the story was very standoffish with its owners.
   **C.** The dog in the story slept under a piano.
   **D.** The dog in the story was always very scared.

4. Who are "these two" mentioned at the beginning of Paragraph 3?

   **A.** The dog and the Master
   **B.** The dog and the Mistress
   **C.** The Master and the Mistress
   **D.** The servants who work for the Master

5. Based on the description in the text, do you think a dog like Lad (who **loves his owners, but is mean to everyone else**) would be good to own? <u>Why</u> or why not?

I think that I would not like a dog like
Lad. For example, if I was going to pick up
Lad from his previous owner Lad
would not like me.

## Selecting the Best Summary

**Directions:** Read each short paragraph below, and then choose the answer that provides the best **summary** of the paragraph. After you've chosen your answer, use the lines below to explain <u>why</u> that choice is the best summary.

1. Jake and Kelly saw a fox when they were coming inside after P.E. class. They told their teacher, Mr. Lee, and he went to the school office to alert the principal. The principal got on the phone to the police station, and animal control officers were on the scene a few minutes later. They caught the fox in a trap and returned it to the woods.

   Which of these is the best summary of the paragraph?

   **A.** Jake and Kelly saved the day by noticing a fox.
   **B.** Mr. Lee should have just called the police himself instead of going to the principal.
   **C.** There was a fox at the school, but thanks to many people's smart actions, no one was hurt.
   **D.** The police responded quickly to a call from the school.

**WHY** is that choice the best summary: Letter c is the best option because it summerizes the paragraph best.

**2.** All museums are filled with knowledge and information, but not all museums are the same. Some museums contain works of art, like paintings, sculptures, and drawings. Other museums are known as museums of "natural history" and contain exhibits about plants, animals, and other aspects of nature. Certain museums focus on human history, too. Those often have clothes, tools, and other important objects from people's daily lives throughout history. Of course, some major museums in big cities contain all these things and more.

Which of these is the best summary of the paragraph?

**A.** The best museums are in the biggest cities.
**B.** Some museums contain natural history while other museums contain human history.
**C.** All museums are interesting and educational places.
**D.** Many museums specialize in a certain kind of history, but some have it all.

**WHY** is that choice the best summary: _It tells us about all the different musems_

 **FITNESS**

Please be aware of your environment and be safe at all times. If you cannot do an exercise, just try your best.

Repeat these **exercises 3 ROUNDS**

**2 - Lunges:** 2 times to each leg.
Note: Use your body weight or books as weight to do leg lunges.

**1 - Abs:** 3 times

**4 - Run:** 50m
Note: Run 25 meters to one side and 25 meters back to the starting position.

**3 - Plank:** 6 sec.

## From "Lad: a Dog"

### By Albert Payson Terhune

The Mistress had crossed the lake to the village, in her canoe, with Lad curled up in a furry heap in the prow. On the return trip, about fifty yards from shore, the canoe struck sharply against a half-floating log that a Fall storm had swept down from the river above the lake. At the same moment a gust of wind caught the canoe's corner. And, like canoes often do, the canvas shell proceeded to turn turtle.

Into the ice-chill waters splashed its two occupants. Lad bobbed to the top, and glanced around at the Mistress to learn if this were a new joke. But, instantly, he saw it was no joke at all, so far as she was concerned.

Wrapped up and cramped by the folds of her heavy outing skirt, the Mistress was making no progress toward the shore. And the dog flung himself through the water toward her with a rush that left his shoulders and half his back above the surface. He grabbed onto the shoulder of her sweater and dragged her back to shore.

1. **Underline** the part of the text that describes why the Mistress and Lad fall into the water.

2. How could Lad's actions be seen as **heroic**?

   Lad saved his owner by lanching himself closer to the Mistress.

20

3. What is Lad's **first** thought when the canoe tips?

   A. That the Mistress is in trouble
   B. That the log attacked them on purpose
   C. That the Mistress is playing a prank
   D. That the canoe is floating away from them

4. According to the text, why does the Mistress have trouble swimming?

   A. She is wearing a lot of heavy clothing
   B. She does not know how to swim
   C. She gets knocked out when the boat tips
   D. She is carrying heavy groceries from the village

5. How would you **summarize** the <u>third paragraph</u> of the passage in your own words?

The Mistress was making no progress toward the shore but Lad lanched himself closer to the Mistress so they could get to the shore.

## Creating a Strong Summary

**Directions:** Read each short paragraph below, then write a one-sentence summary of it on the lines below. As you read, it may be useful to underline main ideas you notice to help you construct your summary.

1. Just because you have an electric dishwasher doesn't mean you never have to wash dishes yourself. Most plates will need to be washed by hand at least a little bit before they go inside the machine. If you don't do that, it will actually make the machine wear out more quickly. Not wiping your dishes ahead of time can also lead to things coming out of the machine with food or sauce still stuck to them instead of being fully clean. Certain kinds of plates, pots, and pans shouldn't go in the dishwasher, so those will always need to be washed by hand.

   **One-Sentence Summary:** Some times you need to use a dishwasher and other time you don't.

2. Mice can crawl into houses through tiny holes in the walls or foundation. Usually, mice will go into a house to find food or shelter, especially during cold and wet times. Once mice are in your house, it can be hard to get them to leave. The first step is to make sure there is no easy food for them to get. If there is no food in your house, the mice will be forced to move on. If that doesn't work, though, you may need to set some traps. If you're uncomfortable with the idea of traps or going near the mice, you may need to call an exterminator, which can be expensive.

   **One-Sentence Summary:** Mice can get into your house but there are many ways to get them out.

**3.** Framing a drawing, photo, or painting is a way to protect your art and make it look really special. When you're picking a frame, it's important to know the size of the work of art that's going inside. You also need to think about whether you want the picture to fill the whole frame or if you want to use a piece of cardboard called a "mat" to create some space between the edge of your picture and the frame. The color of your frame is also important, since it should match the colors in the picture and the room you're hanging it in. With the right frame, any picture becomes a true work of art.

**One-Sentence Summary:** Frames are really important important to art because if you don't have the right frame it could make your artwork not so good.

# FITNESS

Please be aware of your environment and be safe at all times. If you cannot do an exercise, just try your best.

Repeat these **exercises 3 ROUNDS**

**2 - Side Bending:** 5 times to each side. Note: try to touch your feet.

**3 - Tree Pose:** Stay as long as possible. Note: do the same with the other leg.

**1 - Squats:** 5 times. Note: imagine you are trying to sit on a chair.

## Addition Problems

**1.** What is 12 + 16?

  A. 14
  B. 18
  C. 26
  **D. 28** *(circled)*

**2.** Find 34 + 56.

  A. 70
  B. 80
  **C. 90** *(circled)*
  D. 100

**3.** Add 38 to 44.

  A. 72
  **B. 82** *(circled)*
  C. 84
  D. 92

*(handwritten: 38, 44, +, 8 2)*

**4.** What is 27 added to 56?

  **A. 83** *(circled)*
  B. 86
  C. 88
  D. 93

**5.** Calculate.

$$\begin{array}{r} 145 \\ + \phantom{0}21 \\ \hline 166 \end{array}$$

*(166 handwritten)*

**6.** Susan has 87 stamps. Her grandmother gave her another 17 stamps to add to her collection. How many stamps does Susan have in all?

  A. 94
  B. 97
  **C. 104** *(circled)*
  D. 107

*(handwritten: 87, +17, 104)*

**7.** There were 16 potatoes on the table. Father put 24 peppers there, and then 4 tomatoes. How many vegetables are there on the table now?

  *44*

**8.** What is the missing number in the following equation? 45 + __15__ = 60

**9.** Which is NOT a way to make 12?

  A. 6 + 6
  **B. 9 + 2** *(circled)*
  C. 7 + 5
  D. 4 + 8

**10.** How do you make 24?

  A. 11 + 11
  B. 15 + 8
  C. 17 + 5
  **D. 13 + 11** *(circled)*

**11.** What is 36 added to 38?

  _____

**12.** Which sum is greater 6 + 16 or 8 + 12? Show your answer, using a comparison symbol.

  *6+16 = 22*

## Subtraction Problems

**1.** What is 56 - 24?

  A. 36
  B. 34
  **C. 32** *(circled)*
  D. 30

2. Subtract 14 - 10.

4

5. Calculate 18 - 12.

6

3. Find.

$$\begin{array}{r} 7 \\ 8\cancel{2} \\ - 34 \\ \hline 108 \end{array}$$

6. What is the difference between **68** and **34**?
   - A.  38
   - B.  36
   - C.  34 ⟵
   - D.  30

4. What is 16 subtracted from 48?

32

7. What is 150 - 25?
   - A.  100
   - B.  125 ⟵
   - C.  75
   - D.  105

# FITNESS

Please be aware of your environment and be safe at all times. If you cannot do an exercise, just try your best.

Repeat these **exercises 3 ROUNDS**

**1 - Bend forward:** 10 times.
Note: try to touch your feet. Make sure to keep your back straight and if needed you can bend your knees.

**2 - Lunges:** 3 times to each leg.
Note: Use your body weight or books as weight to do leg lunges.

**3 - Plank:** 6 sec.

**4 - Abs:**
10 times

## Subtraction Problems

1. Find the difference between **550** and **250**.

   ~~~~~~~~~~~~~~~~~

2. There were **43** cucumbers in the fridge. Marie used **4** cucumbers to make a salad. How many cucumbers are there in the fridge now?

   ~~~~~~~~~~~~~~~~~

3. Father had **677** baseball cards. He sold **71** of them. How many does he have now?

   A. 670
   B. 607
   C. 616
   D. 606

4. What is the missing number in the following equations?

   A. 43 - ~~~~~ = 27
   B. ~~~~~ - 12 = 4
   C. 35 - 19 = ~~~~~
   D. 57 - ~~~~~ = 41

   ~~~~~~~~~~~~~~~~~

5. Subtract **35** from **105**.

   ~~~~~~~~~~~~~~~~~

## Multiplication Problems

1. Write an equation to express the array and then find the number of shapes.

   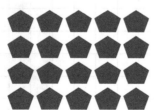

   ~~~~~~~~~~~~~~~~~

2. Which expression describes the model?

   A. 3 + 5
   B. 3 x 5
   C. 3 x 4
   D. 5 x 4

3. Complete the multiplication sentence that describes the model ~~~~~ x 4 = 16.

   ~~~~~~~~~~~~~~~~~

4. What is 6 x 5?
   A. 12
   B. 18
   C. 25
   D. 30

5. Find the product of 12 and 3.

   A. 15
   B. 24
   C. 36
   D. 40

6. Which number sentence below is true?

   A. 3 x 9 = 21
   B. 5 x 7 = 25
   C. 14 x 2 = 26
   D. 8 x 0 = 0

7. What is 20 times 4?

   ~~~~~~~~~~~~~~~~~

8. What is the product of 42 and 2?

   A. 44          C. 62
   B. 84          D. 64

9. Which expression describes the model?

   A. 9 x 3
   B. 9 + 3
   C. 3 + 9
   D. 3 x 8

10. Find the product of 20 and 8.

    A. 16         C. 160
    B. 28         D. 280

11. Calculate 8 x 5.

12. Which expression represents 6 x 12?

    A. 12 + 12 + 12 + 12 + 12
    B. 12 + 12 + 12 + 12 + 12 + 12
    C. 6 + 12 + 6 + 12 + 6 + 12
    D. 6 + 6 + 6 + 6 + 6 + 6 + 12

## Division Problems

1. What is 20 ÷ 4?

   A. 15          C. 5
   B. 10          D. 4

2. Find the quotient of 36 ÷ 3.

   A. 18          C. 11
   B. 12          D. 6

3. What is the quotient of 11 ÷ 1?

   _____

4. What is the quotient when 40 is divided by 10?

   _____

5. Find 14 ÷ 2.

   A. 12          C. 11
   B. 10          D. 7

# FITNESS

Please be aware of your environment and be safe at all times. If you cannot do an exercise, just try your best.

Repeat these **exercises 3 ROUNDS**

**1 - High Plank:** 6 sec.

**2 - Chair:** 10 sec.
Note: sit on an imaginary chair, keep your back straight.

**3 - Waist Hooping:** 10 times. Note: if you do not have a hoop, pretend you have an imaginary hoop and rotate your hips 10 times.

**4 - Abs:** 10 times

## Division Problems

1. Complete the division sentence that describes the model. _____ ÷ 3 = 4.

2. Which number sentence below is true?
   A. $15 \div 3 = 6$
   B. $24 \div 4 = 6$
   C. $33 \div 1 = 32$
   D. $16 \div 8 = 3$

3. Which of the following statements is false?
   A. $12 \div 6 = 6$
   B. $14 \div 7 = 2$
   C. $30 \div 3 = 10$
   D. $63 \div 1 = 63$

4. Which equation can be solved by knowing that 9 x 8 = 72?
   A. $9 \div 72 =$
   B. $8 \div 72 =$
   C. $72 \div 8 =$
   D. $72 \times 8 =$

5. What is the quotient when 27 is divided by 27? _____

6. What is the missing number in the following equations?
$$12 \div \text{\_\_\_\_} = 2$$
$$36 \div \text{\_\_\_\_} = 6$$
$$\text{\_\_\_\_} \div 3 = 2$$
$$18 \div 3 = \text{\_\_\_\_}$$

7. What is the missing number in this equation $27 \div \text{\_\_\_\_} = 9$?

## Word problems: Mix of add/subtract/multiply/divide

1. Iren had 19 yellow beads. She used 7 of them. How many beads does Iren have now?

2. Marie bought 7 apples. Then she went back and bought 14 apples more. At home she divided them equally between three children. How many apples did each child get?
   A. 4
   B. 5
   C. 6
   D. 7

3. Diana had 35 stones. She gave 19 of them to her brother Timmy. How many stones does Diana have now?
   A. 15
   B. 16
   C. 17
   D. 18

4. A fast food restaurant sold seventy-two cupcakes and fourteen burritos. How many more cupcakes than burritos were sold?
   A. 48
   B. 52
   C. 58
   D. 62

5. Greg added 8 x 3 to 2 x 4. What was the sum that he got?

   A. 24          C. 30
   B. 28          D. 32

6. Nick studies 10 hours a week. If each study session lasts 2 hours long, how many study sessions does Nick have in a week?

7. Megan had twelve pencils in her desk and two times more in her backpack. How many pencils did she have in total?

   A. 28          C. 40
   B. 36          D. 44

8. Frank picked 50 pears from the tree. If Kate picked three times more pears than Frank, how many did they pick up in total?

   A. 100         C. 200
   B. 150         D. 250

9. A pet store had fourteen guinea pigs and 9 rabbits. How many animals did the pet store have in total?

10. Zach spent twenty-two minutes playing at school and thirty-two minutes playing at home. How many minutes total did he spend playing?

11. A chef can cook 15 meals in three minutes. If he cooked 45 meals, how long did it take him?

    A. 7 minutes
    B. 8 minutes
    C. 9 minutes
    D. 10 minutes

12. For his birthday party Chris spent ninety-two dollars on food and twelve dollars on drinks. How much did Chris spend in total?

YOGA

Please be aware of your environment and be safe at all times. If you cannot do an exercise, just try your best.

**1 - Down**
Dog: 10 sec.

**2 - Bend Down:** 10 sec.

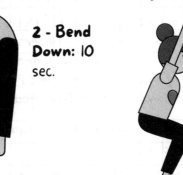

**3 - Chair:** 10 sec.

**4 - Child Pose:** 20 sec.

**5 - Shavasana:** as long as you can. Note: think of happy moments and relax your mind.

# EXPERIMENT

## Seed Dispersers

You probably already know that plants grow from seeds. However, you've probably never thought too much about how seeds are spread so plants can grow in new locations. Animals known as **seed dispersers** play an important role in the creation of new plants. **Seed dispersers** eat fruit that contain plant seeds (such as apples, strawberries, etc.) and then spread that seed to new places when they go to the bathroom.

Today, we'll be creating a small model of an ecosystem to illustrate how seeds are spread.

### Materials:

- A small cardboard box (a cereal box is ideal)
- Construction paper
- Art supplies (markers, colored pencils, etc.)
- A paper cup
- Glue
- Scissors
- An adult
- Some small seeds (sesame seeds work great!)

### Procedure:

1. Flatten your cereal box to create the base you will build your ecosystem on top of. If you want, you can cut the sides of the box (ask an adult for help!) to help you create some trees in Step 3.

2. Using construction paper, cover the large, flat side of the cereal box to create a natural setting. There should be both **land** and **water** (using different colors of construction paper or coloring a white sheet of paper would both work). Most of your area should be land, but try to make at least one lake, pond, or river as well.

3. Using construction paper (or cardboard harvested from the box), create three small trees and glue, or tape, them into your ecosystem. These represent fruit trees.

4. Use the paper cup to create a mountain in your ecosystem. You can color the cup, cover it in construction paper to make it look more like a mountain, or just leave it as is.

5. Now that your ecosystem is complete, grab a handful of seeds and pretend that you are a **squirrel**. Start with your fingers holding the seeds near one of the trees (where the squirrel would have eaten fruit), and then move your hand around the ecosystem at ground level, imagining how a squirrel might run around or explore the area. As you move your hand around, occasionally drop a few seeds to represent the squirrel going to the bathroom.

6. After you've distributed all your squirrel seeds, take a look at the ecosystem. Where did the seeds wind up?

7. Pick up another handful of seeds and now imagine that you are a **bird**. Start at the **top** of one of the trees and fly around your ecosystem, occasionally dropping seeds to represent the bird going to the bathroom. Remember to "fly" with your hand up high above the ecosystem.

8. After you've distributed all your bird seeds, take a look at the ecosystem. Where did the seeds wind up?

9. Answer the questions below. Then clean up any spilled seeds. **Save your ecosystem** since we'll be using it again next week.

**Follow-Up Questions:**

1. Based on what you saw, how do birds and squirrels scatter seeds in different ways?

_____

_____

_____

2. Based on what you saw, why might it be difficult for a large number of seeds to grow on mountains?

_____

_____

_____

# YOGA

Please be aware of your environment and be safe at all times. If you cannot do an exercise, just try your best.

**1 - Tree Pose:** Stay as long as possible. Note: do on one leg then on another.

**2 - Down Dog:** 10 sec.

**3 - Stretching:** Stay as long as possible. Note: do on one leg then on another.

**5 - Book Pose:** 6 sec. Note: Keep your core tight. Legs should be across from your eyes.

**4 - Lower Plank:** 6 sec. Note: Keep your back straight and body tight.

**6 - Shavasana:** 5 min. Note: this pose is very important and provides you with long term benefits. Try not to skip this. Close your eyes and imagine who you want to be and what your goals are! Always think happy thoughts.

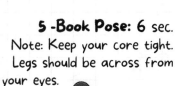
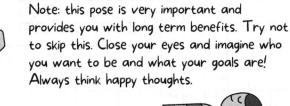

**Task:** Which route (Route 1, 2, or 3) should Manny the Bear take to meet his friend at the end of the maze?

# FEBRUARY
# WEEK 2

February is the month of love! There are 28 days in the month of February. However, there are 29 days during a leap year. Leap years happen every 4 years. The next leap year will be on February 29, 2024.

Last week, we introduced the idea of a **summary** and you practiced summarizing paragraphs. This week, we're going to ramp things up by lengthening the texts you're summarizing. Being able to summarize a paragraph is an important skill, but summarizing is actually the most useful when you're dealing with long, complex texts.

Luckily, you already have all the tools you need to create a successful summary of any text, no matter how long it is! You just need to focus on **main ideas** and think about how you'd explain the text to someone with no prior knowledge about it.

### Key Terms:

Summary: A brief explanation of a text's main points or ideas
- It could be...
  - A book
  - A movie
  - An episode of a TV show
  - Something that happened in real life
  - ...pretty much anything!

Summarize: To read something (like a book or article) and create a summary based on it.

### Hints & Strategies for Creating a Summary:

- Read or review the text you are summarizing **closely**
- Look for **main ideas**
  - What does the author present at the beginning?
  - What ideas get repeated?
- Focus on the information people **need to know**, not things that are *nice* to know.
- Don't include too much information
  - Information overload defeats the whole purpose of creating a summary!

**Hints & Strategies for Summarizing Texts with More than One Paragraph:**

- Try to read and summarize the **first paragraph first**
    - Often, the first paragraph will lay out the main ideas
        - This is called an introduction (more on this in a few weeks!)
- Read each paragraph <u>one at a time</u> and summarize each one in a single sentence.
    - Once you've done this for each paragraph, reread each of your one-sentence summaries and see if you can follow the flow of ideas from paragraph to paragraph
        - If you **can**, you have a strong summary!
- **Don't** include every single detail, example, or minor fact in your summary
    - The goal is to create something <u>short and useful!</u>

## From "Blackfoot Lodge Tales"

### By George Bird Grinnell

In those days there was a chief named Owl Bear. He was a great chief, very brave and generous. One night he had a dream: he saw many dead bodies of the enemy lying about, and he knew that he must go to war. So he called out for a feast, and after the people had eaten, he said:—

"I had a strong dream last night. I went to war against the Snakes, and killed many of their warriors. So the signs are good, and I feel that I must go. Let us have a big party now, and I will be the leader. We will start to-morrow night."

Then he told two old men to go out in the camp and shout the news, so that all might know. A big party was made up. Two hundred men, they say, went with this chief to war. The first night they travelled only a little way, for they were not used to walking, and soon got tired.

In the morning the chief got up early and went and made a sacrifice, and when he came back to the others, some said, "Come now, tell us your dream of this night."

"I dreamed good," said Owl Bear. "I had a good dream. We will have good luck."

But many others said they had bad dreams.

1. Underline the part of the passage that suggests or predicts something **bad** might happen to Owl Bear and his warriors?

2. Based on the passage, why does Owl Bear believe he should go to war?

    **A.** Enemies have attacked his people.

    **B.** He has a dream about his enemies being defeated.

    **C.** He wants to get revenge for something bad his enemies did in the past.

    **D.** He is an angry person and likes violence.

3. What detail in the **third paragraph** shows that Owl Bear's warriors might not be as strong and prepared for battle as he thinks?

_____

_____

_____

4. According to the story, about how many warriors traveled with Owl Bear?

   **A.** Around 100
   **B.** Around 200
   **C.** Around 500
   **D.** Around 1000

5. <u>**Summarize**</u> the passage in 2-3 sentences:

_____

_____

_____

_____

_____

## Summarizing a Multi-Paragraph Text

**Directions:** Read the 3-paragraph passage below and answer the questions that follow to create a **summary**.

### From Lola; Or, the Thought and Speech of Animals

### by Henny Kindermann

It was in the year 1904 that the first experiments towards understanding an animal's ability to think were brought into public light. Wilhelm von Osten then introduced his stallion Hans II to all who seemed interested in the subject, and the most opposed opinions were soon rife with regard to the abilities of this horse, to which von Osten maintained he had succeeded in teaching both spelling and arithmetic.

The animal's mental activity was said to lie in a simple form of thinking, called into being and intensified by means of a certain amount of instruction. Von Osten, who had been a schoolmaster, had previously spent some fourteen years in testing the intelligence of two other horses before he ventured to make his experiences public, and the performances of these animals were not only remarkable, but of far-reaching importance.

Hans I, aged twelve, died in 1905. He had never appeared in public, since his abilities had been relatively modest. He had, nevertheless, been able to count up to five, as well as carry out quite a number of verbal instructions. It was Hans II, however, that convinced his master—as early as 1902—of his ability to comprehend a far greater range of the German alphabet (when written), as well as to recognize a certain number of colors.

1. According to the passage, what made Hans I and Hans II special horses?

_____

_____

_____

2. Based on the passage, write a short **summary** of what Wilhelm von Osten was researching in his work:

_____

_____

_____

# FITNESS

Please be aware of your environment and be safe at all times. If you cannot do an exercise, just try your best.

Repeat these
**exercises**
**3 ROUNDS**

**1 - Abs:**
3 times

**2 - Lunges:** 2 times to each leg.
Note: Use your body weight or books as weight to do leg lunges.

**3 - Plank:** 6 sec.

**4 - Run:** 50m
Note: Run **25** meters to one side and **25** meters back to the starting position.

## From "Blackfoot Lodge Tales"

### By George Bird Grinnell

They travelled on, and travelled on, always having bad dreams, until they came close to the Elk River. Then the oldest warrior said, "Come, my chief, let us all turn back. We still have bad dreams. We cannot have good luck."

"No," replied Owl Bear, "I will not turn back."

Then they were going to seize him and tie his hands, for they had talked of this before. They thought to tie him and make him go back with them. Then the chief got very angry. He put an arrow on his bow, and said: "Do not touch me. You are my relations; but if any of you try to tie me, I will kill you. Now I am ashamed. My relations are cowards and will turn back. I have told you I have always dreamed good, and that we would have good luck. Now I don't care; I am covered with shame. I am going now to the Snake camp and will give them my body. I am ashamed."

They said no more. They turned back homeward, and the chief was all alone. His heart was very sad as he travelled on, and he was much ashamed, for his relations had left him.

1. Which of these is the best **summary** of Paragraph 3?

   **A.** Owl Bear's warriors deserted him because they did not want to help him anymore.

   **B.** Owl Bear sent his warriors home because he decided they were not brave enough.

   **C.** Owl Bear had a bad dream that told him the war would end badly.

   **D.** Owl Bear's warriors tried to capture him and force him to go home, but he ignored and scolded them.

2. **Underline** the place in the text where the warriors explain why they think Owl Bear should go home.

40

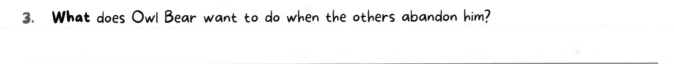
3. **What** does Owl Bear want to do when the others abandon him?

_____

_____

4. Why does Owl Bear say he is ashamed?

   **A.** He thinks the warriors (who are also his relatives) are cowards.

   **B.** He thinks the warriors (who are also his relatives) are evil.

   **C.** He thinks the warriors (who are also his relatives) don't respect him anymore.

   **D.** He thinks the warriors (who are also his relatives) have joined his enemies.

5. Based on Day 1's passage and this passage, what do you **predict** might happen to Owl Bear if he continues with his "war?"

_____

_____

_____

_____

## Summarizing a Multi-Paragraph Text

**Directions:** Read the two-paragraph passage below and answer the questions that follow to create a summary.

# From Lola; Or, the Thought and Speech of Animals
## by Henny Kindermann

Lola had been four days with me—accompanying me through the house, and about the farm, at first on a lead, but soon without. Her extreme animation verged on wildness; I was struck with her elastic temperament and her constant attentiveness, and it seemed to me that this dog would hardly be able to sit still for five minutes. She already knew "yes," and "no," and in my joy at possessing a dog able to answer me, I put so many questions to her that I began to be afraid I might do her some injury. I was, in fact, so afraid, so in doubt as to my understanding, and so alive to my responsibilities in the matter, that I often wished I had not accepted the dog at all. I did not even know whether I could "teach"—much less whether I could "teach a dog," whom, moreover, no hereditary "urge" would induce to attend school once she knew that this would mean having to work and be attentive!

Doubts as to whether the dog understood me; in what way she understood me; what sort of creature a dog really was—whether she could "think," "feel," or even whether she was capable of hearing in the same way as we hear; able to see in the same way that we see with our eyes; whether she already possessed some cognition of the human language, and whether this possessed any meaning for her? For all at once I knew that I knew nothing. That I had not even the least idea as to the best manner to assume, whether I ought to be gentle or strict—these are but a few of the difficulties I found myself beset by.

1.  In **Paragraph 1**, what kind of <u>activity</u> is the narrator <u>describing</u> doing with the dog Lola?

_____

2.  In **Paragraph 2**, what <u>question</u> is the narrator asking about Lola (and dogs in general)?

_____

_____

3.  Based on your previous two answers, how would you summarize this passage in one sentence?

_____

_____

_____

# FITNESS

Please be aware of your environment and be safe at all times. If you cannot do an exercise, just try your best.

Repeat these **exercises 3 ROUNDS**

**2 - Side Bending:**
5 times to each side. Note: try to touch your feet.

**3 - Tree Pose:**
Stay as long as possible.
Note: do the same with the other leg.

**1 - Squats: 5** times.
Note: imagine you are trying to sit on a chair.

## Place values

1.  What number is shown?

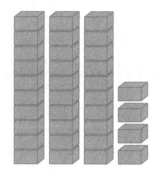

   A. 34        C. 43
   B. 36        D. 44

2.  Which digit is in the tens place?
   356
   _____

3.  Regroup. Write a number from 0 to 9 on each line.

   2 hundreds + 13 tens + 26 ones = _____ hundreds + _____ tens + _____ ones
   _____

4.  What is the value of the underlined digit?
   76<u>8</u>

   A. 8        C. 800
   B. 80       D. 8,000

5.  What is the value of the underlined digit?
   <u>9</u>26

   A. 9        C. 900
   B. 90       D. 9,000

6.  Write the missing number. 5 hundreds + _____ tens + 3 ones = 583.

   A. 5        C. 3
   B. 8        D. 4

7.  Which place-value model shows 81?

   A.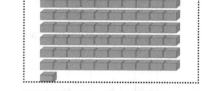

   B.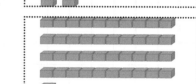

   C.

   D.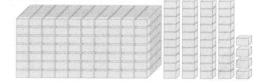

8.  Which place-value model shows 634?

   A.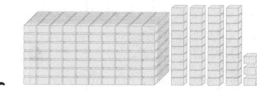

   B.

   C.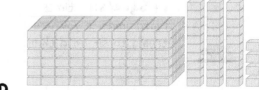

   D.

44

9. Determine the numbers shown in the boxes.

| Hundreds | Tens | Ones |
|----------|------|------|

~~~~~~~~~~~~~~~~~~~~~~~~

10. Use the blocks to determine the total quantities.

_____ ones = _____ tens = _____ hundreds

11. Determine how many groups of 100 can be created from the blocks shown.

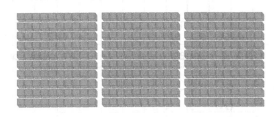

~~~~~~~~~~~~~~~~~~~~~~~~

12. Find the value the set of blocks represents.

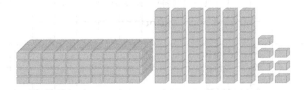

A. 366
B. 457
C. 467
D. 567

---

# FITNESS

Please be aware of your environment and be safe at all times. If you cannot do an exercise, just try your best.

Repeat these **exercises 3 ROUNDS**

**1 - Bend forward:** 10 times. Note: try to touch your feet. Make sure to keep your back straight and if needed you can bend your knees.

**2 - Lunges:** 3 times to each leg. Note: Use your body weight or books as weight to do leg lunges.

**3 - Plank:** 6 sec.

**4 - Abs:** 10 times

## Standard form vs. expanded form

1. Choose an option in which the number **683** is represented in an expanded form.

    A. 60 + 80 + 3
    B. 80 + 3 + 600
    C. 800 + 6 + 30
    D. 3 + 600 + 800

2. Which of the following answer choices represents the number four hundred thirty-six in standard form?

    A. 463
    B. 346
    C. 436
    D. 634

3. Choose the standard form of the number 3 + 600 + 70.

    A. 367
    B. 673
    C. 637
    D. 736

4. The number **916** in expanded form can be written as:

    A. 10 + 900 + 6
    B. 60 + 100 + 9
    C. 100 + 90 + 60
    D. 900 + 60 + 1

5. Choose the standard form of the number 40 + 3 + 500.

    A. 435
    B. 453
    C. 534
    D. 543

6. How do you write this number using digits?

    three hundred eighty-one _____
    nine hundred thirty-four _____
    five hundred twenty-seven _____
    one hundred ninety-two _____

7. The number **832** in expanded form can be written as:

    A. 30 + 80 + 20
    B. 300 + 2 + 80
    C. 2 + 800 + 30
    D. 800 + 3 + 20

8. The number **769** in expanded form can be written as:

    A. 700 + 6 + 9
    B. 60 + 90 + 7
    C. 90 + 700 + 6
    D. 60 + 9 + 700

9. Which option contains the number **226** in expanded form?

    A. 20 + 6 + 20
    B. 6 + 20 + 200
    C. 60 + 2 + 200
    D. 2 + 200 + 6

10. The number three hundred and nine written in standard form is

    _____

11. Which combination of numbers is the expanded form of 476?

|    | Hundreds | Tens | Ones |
|----|----------|------|------|
| A. | 7        | 6    | 4    |
| B. | 9        | 7    | 6    |
| C. | 4        | 7    | 6    |
| D. | 6        | 4    | 7    |

12. Write the number two hundred and thirty-three.

13. Write 316 in words.

14. What is 70 + 200 + 5 in standard form?

15. Write the missing number.

    8 hundreds + 3 tens + 7 ones = _____

16. Write the missing numbers.

    _____ hundreds + _____ tens + _____ ones = 916.

17. Determine the number shown in the boxes.

| Hundreds | Tens | Ones |
|----------|------|------|
| 8        | 2    | 0    |

# FITNESS

Please be aware of your environment and be safe at all times. If you cannot do an exercise, just try your best.

Repeat these exercises **3 ROUNDS**

**1 - High Plank:** 6 sec.

**2 - Chair:** 10 sec.
Note: sit on an imaginary chair, keep your back straight.

**4 - Abs:** 10 times

**3 - Waist Hooping:** 10 times. Note: if you do not have a hoop, pretend you have an imaginary hoop and rotate your hips 10 times.

## Rounding to nearest 10 and 100

1. How many balls are there in the picture? Estimate.

   A. 10
   B. 20
   C. 30
   D. 40

2. How many cubes are there in the picture? Estimate.

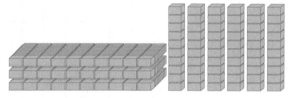

   A. 200
   B. 300
   C. 400
   D. 500

3. What is 68 rounded to the nearest ten?

   _____

4. What is 74 rounded to the nearest hundred?

   _____

5. Which addition problem has a sum of about 80?

   A. 26 + 67
   B. 29 + 60
   C. 33 + 45
   D. 46 + 44

6. How many stars are there in the picture? Estimate.

   A. 30
   B. 40
   C. 50
   D. 60

7. Which place value do you need to round in the number 378 to get 380?

   A. Nearest ten
   B. Nearest hundred

8. Round 651 to the nearest hundred.

   _____

9. Which of the following numbers could be rounded to 400?

   A. 356
   B. 468
   C. 337
   D. 349

10. What is 768 rounded to the nearest hundred?

    _____

11. What is 295 rounded to the nearest ten?

    _____

12. Round 681 to the nearest hundred.

    _____

13. Round **654** and **643** to the nearest ten. Write a number sentence using those two rounded numbers and a comparison symbol.

14. Round **726** to the nearest hundred.

15. Round **339** and **354** to the nearest hundred. Write a number sentence using those two rounded numbers and a comparison symbol.

16. How many cubes are there in the picture? Estimate.

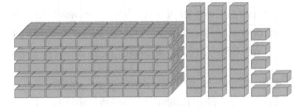

A. 520
B. 530
C. 540
D. 550

17. Round **996** to the nearest ten.

 YOGA

Please be aware of your environment and be safe at all times. If you cannot do an exercise, just try your best.

**1 - Down Dog:** 10 sec.

**2 - Bend Down:** 10 sec.

**3 - Chair:** 10 sec.

**4 - Child Pose:** 20 sec.

**5 - Shavasana:** as long as you can. Note: think of happy moments and relax your mind.

## Pollinators

Last week, we explored how animals like **birds** and **squirrels** help spread seeds so new plants can grow. Remember, those **seed dispersers** got those seeds by eating fruit! This week, we'll look at how other animals help plants create food through a process known as pollination.

**Pollination** is the spreading of pollen. In order to create fruit, plants need to combine their pollen with the pollen of other plants. Animals known as **pollinators** help spread pollen by landing on plants to drink their nectar. Each time an animal does this, a little pollen sticks to their body, which is then transferred to the next plant they land on. We'll explore that process today.

### Materials:

- Your ecosystem from the Week 1 experiment
- Cotton swabs
- Cotton balls
- Glue
- Glitter (ideally, a few different colors)

### Procedure:

1. Set up your ecosystem as you had it last week. It should have some **land**, some **water**, a mountain, and a few **trees** on it. If you want to make any repairs or changes to your ecosystem, this is the time to do it.

2. Gently pull a few cotton balls apart so they create a wide, fuzzy surface. Using a little glue, attach a few cotton balls to your ecosystem. These represent small plants, bushes, and shrubs with flowers.

3. Once you've added your "flowering plants" to the ecosystem, put a little glitter on top of them (don't glue it down). If you have some different colored glitter, try putting different colors on the various cotton balls around the ecosystem. You should also add some glitter to the **fruit trees** you added last week.

4. Pick up one of the cotton swabs and pretend you are a **butterfly**. Start near one of the flowering plants in your ecosystem and rub one end of the swab against it until you pick up some of the glitter. This represents the butterfly getting pollen on it.

5. Holding the swab, "fly" your butterfly to the nearest tree or flowering plant and rub your swab on that plant as well. Repeat this process until your butterfly has gathered pollen from several different plants. Remember: a butterfly is small, so it probably can't fly all the way across your ecosystem!

6. Once your butterfly's flight is complete, closely examine your swab, as well as the different plants you touched with it. If you used different colored glitter, it should be easy to see that the pollination process has occurred!

7. Set your butterfly swab aside and pick up a second swab. This one represents a **bat**. Start your bat in one of the tall trees and rub your swab against that tree to pick up some pollen.

# EXPERIMENT

8. Holding the swab, "fly" your bat to another tree or flowering plant. Bats are much bigger and stronger than butterflies, so the bat can fly long distances across the ecosystem. If you want, with each stop your bat makes, rub the swab in glitter to pollinate.

9. Once your bat's flight is complete, closely examine your swab, as well as the different plants you touched with it. If you used different color glitter, it should be easy to observe the pollination process!

10. Clean up all your materials. You do not need to keep your ecosystem any longer, unless you want to.

### Follow-Up Questions:

1. How do bats and butterflies perform **similar** work as pollinators?

_____

_____

_____

2. How are bats and butterflies **different** as pollinators?

_____

_____

_____

 YOGA

Please be aware of your environment and be safe at all times. If you cannot do an exercise, just try your best.

**1 - Tree Pose:**
Stay as long as possible.
Note: do on one leg then on another.

**2 - Down Dog:** 10 sec.

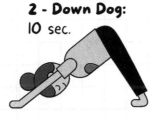

**3 - Stretching:**
Stay as long as possible. Note: do on one leg then on another.

**5 - Book Pose:** 6 sec.
Note: Keep your core tight. Legs should be across from your eyes.

**6 - Shavasana:** 5 min.
Note: this pose is very important and provides you with long term benefits. Try not to skip this. Close your eyes and imagine who you want to be and what your goals are! Always think happy thoughts.

**4 - Lower Plank:** 6 sec.
Note: Keep your back straight and body tight.

**Task**: Which piece below will complete the picture?
How do you know?

1

2

3

4

5

# MARCH
# WEEK 3

Yay! March is when spring starts and animals start to wake up from hibernation. Daylight Savings also happens on the second Sunday in March when the clock moves forward 1 hour.

# OVERVIEW OF ENGLISH CONCEPTS

## Events in a Sequence

Recently, we've talked a lot about **summarizing**: taking long texts and boiling them down to their main ideas. Knowing what the main ideas are isn't enough to claim you have a full understanding of any text, though. You also need to know what **sequence** those main ideas were organized into. A **sequence** is an order or a series of steps. Any time you follow instructions, you're going through a sequence. Every time you count from 1 to 10 or say the alphabet, that's a **sequence**!

The **sequence** things happen in is one of the most important aspects of any story or movie. We generally call this the **plot**. If you can't follow the plot, stories can be very hard to understand! Even in informational text, recognizing what order ideas are presented in and why they are laid out that way makes ideas more accessible and easy to learn.

### Key Terms:

Plot: All the events of a story, arranged in sequence
- In a sentence: "I found the **plot** of that movie hard to follow."

Sequence: An order in which things happen
- In a sentence: "If you dial the correct sequence of numbers, my cell phone will ring."

### Recognizing Sequences in Literary Text (Fiction)

Part of understanding a story is recognizing the importance of the order things happen in, not just focusing on all the things that happened. When you're **reading** a story or **watching** a movie or video, ask yourselves the following questions to help you focus on the plot and sequence of events:

1. **WHAT** is happening in the story?

   - What **actions** or **events** are taking place?
   - How does **one thing lead to another** in the story?
     - How do decisions or actions by characters early on affect things later?

2. **WHO** is involved in each "scene" of the story?

   - Focus on **who did what**, <u>not</u> just "what happened"
     - Complex books often involve characters knowing different things or having different experiences. For those characters to be clear to you, you need to know who was involved in what.

3. **HOW** do these events affect the characters?

   - Always think about how characters grow or change during a story

# OVERVIEW OF ENGLISH CONCEPTS

## Recognizing Sequences in Informational Texts (Non-Fiction)

Sequence is different in informational text because they're **supposed to be** <u>as clear as</u> <u>possible</u>! That means less worrying about following a story and more focus on building ideas. When you're reading an informational text, here are some questions to focus on:

1.  **<u>Why</u>** is this text organized the way it is?

    *   Is it laid out in the **order** things happened? Is it broken down into **topics**? Is it supposed to **build** from simple ideas to complex ideas?

    *   Once you understand why the author presents things in a certain order, it makes the text easier to follow and gain valuable information from.

2.  What **<u>other information</u>** is the author giving me to help me understand things on a deeper level?

    *   A lot of times, authors of informational texts will use **lists, timelines, charts,** or other ways to communicate ideas without just using words. These can also contain important information about **what order** things happened in or **what steps** certain processes follow.

## From "Blackfoot Lodge Tales"

### By George Bird Grinnell

This happened long ago. In those days the people were hungry. No buffalo nor antelope were seen on the prairie. The deer and the elk trails were covered with grass and leaves; not even a rabbit could be found in the brush. Then the people prayed, saying: "Oh, Old Man, help us now, or we shall die. The buffalo and deer are gone. Uselessly we kindle the morning fires; useless are our arrows; our knives stick fast in the sheaths."

Then Old Man started out to find the game, and he took with him a young man, the son of a chief. For many days they travelled the prairies and ate nothing but berries and roots. One day they climbed a high ridge, and when they had reached the top, they saw, far off by a stream, a single lodge.

"What kind of a person can it be," said the young man, "who camps there all alone, far from friends?"

"That," said Old Man, "is the one who has hidden all the buffalo and deer from the people. He has a wife and a little son."

Then they went close to the lodge, and Old Man changed himself into a little dog, and he said, "That is I." Then the young man changed himself into a curved stick, like the kind people used to dig up roots, and he said, "That is I."

1. **Underline** the part of the passage that shows the main problem that the characters are dealing with.

2. Which of these animals is <u>not</u> specifically mentioned in the story?

   **A.** Rabbit

   **B.** Elk

   **C.** Buffalo

   **D.** Squirrel

3. Which of these events happened **last** in the story?

   **A.** The people asked the Old Man for help.

   **B.** The chief's son turned into a root digger.

   **C.** The Old Man brought the chief's son to the high ridge.

   **D.** The Old Man turned into a dog.

**3.** How can the reader tell that the **Old Man** is a very important character in the story?

_____

_____

_____

**4. Summarize** the passage in **2-4** sentences:

_____

_____

_____

_____

_____

_____

_____

## Thinking About Sequence

**Directions:** Answer the following questions by imagining each situation and thinking about the **sequence** (order) of events:

1. If you wanted to **cook dinner**, which of these would be the best <u>first</u> step?

   **A.** Boiling water

   **B.** Deciding what you want to make

   **C.** Gathering ingredients

   **D.** Setting the table

2. If you were **getting ready to go to school** in the morning, which of these would make sense to do <u>last</u>?

   **A.** Brush your teeth

   **B.** Eat breakfast

   **C.** Get dressed

   **D.** Put on your backpack

3. Based on your understanding of **sequence**, which of these things would probably happen <u>in the middle</u> of a book or movie that told a story?

   **A.** The main character lives peacefully in a world where nothing is wrong.

   **B.** The main character defeats the villain.

   **C.** The main character travels to find the villain.

   **D.** The main character lives happily ever after.

**WEEK 3 DAY 1**

4. Which of these events is **not important** to the rest of the sequence that's being described?

   A. The soccer game was tied **2-2** at the half.
   B. Michelle's family was 15 minutes late to the game.
   C. Out of nowhere, Christine scored a winning goal in the final seconds.
   D. The entire second half was back-and-forth, with nobody scoring.

5. Which of these events is **not important** to the rest of the sequence that's being described?

   A. Plumbers are more expensive than fixing things yourself.
   B. If your sink is clogged, you can try some at-home drain cleaner.
   C. If none of that works, try calling a plumber.
   D. You can also use small tools from the hardware store to try and clear the drain yourself.

## FITNESS

Please be aware of your environment and be safe at all times. If you cannot do an exercise, just try your best.

Repeat these
**exercises**
**3 ROUNDS**

**1 - Abs:** 3 times

**2 - Lunges: 2** times to each leg.
Note: Use your body weight or books as weight to do leg lunges.

**4 - Run: 50**m
Note: Run 25 meters to one side and 25 meters back to the starting position.

**3 - Plank: 6** sec.

## From "Blackfoot Lodge Tales"

### By George Bird Grinnell

### (Continued from Day 1's Passage)

Now the little boy, playing about, found the dog, and he carried it to his father, saying, "Look! See what a pretty little dog I have found." "Throw it away," said his father; "it is not a dog." And the little boy cried, but his father made him carry the dog away. Then the boy found the root-digger; and, again picking up the dog, he carried them both to the lodge, saying, "Look, mother! See the pretty root-digger I have found!"

"Throw them both away," said his father; "that is not a stick, that is not a dog."

"I want that stick," said the woman; "let our son have the little dog."

"Very well," said her husband, "but remember, if trouble comes, you bring it on yourself and on our son." Then he sent his wife and son off to pick berries; and when they were out of sight, he went out and killed a buffalo cow, and brought the meat into the lodge and covered it up, and the bones and skin he threw in the creek. When his wife returned, he gave her some of the meat to roast; and while they were eating the little boy fed the dog three times, and when he gave it more, his father took the meat away, saying, "That is not a dog, you shall not feed it more."

1. **Underline** at least two places in the text where the boy's father shows he understands that something magical is going on.

2. Based on this passage and Day 1's passage, why is the father right to distrust the dog and stick?

_____

_____

_____

3. Which of these describes the **son's** attitude in this passage?

    **A.** Nervous

    **B.** Suspicious

    **C.** Excited

    **D.** Confused

4. Which of these events happened **last** in the passage?

    **A.** The son fed the dog

    **B.** The father killed a buffalo

    **C.** The woman said she wanted the stick

    **D.** The husband let the woman and son keep the dog and stick

5. **Why** do you think the father/husband sends his family away before he kills the buffalo at the beginning of the final paragraph?

_____

_____

_____

_____

## Sequencing Events

**Directions:** Read each situation and take a few minutes to **brainstorm** what steps you'd need to take in order to achieve the goal. Once you've settled on the steps you'd need, write them on the lines below.

1. Getting to the closest park (from your house):

_____

_____

_____

_____

_____

_____

_____

_____

2. Putting a puzzle together:

_____

_____

_____

_____

_____

_____

_____

_____

**3.** Making a paper airplane:

_____

_____

_____

_____

_____

_____

_____

# FITNESS

Please be aware of your environment and be safe at all times. If you cannot do an exercise, just try your best.

Repeat these
**exercises**
**3 ROUNDS**

**2 - Side Bending:**
5 times to each side. Note: try to touch your feet.

**3 - Tree Pose:**
Stay as long as possible.
Note: do the same with the other leg.

**1 - Squats:** 5 times.
Note: imagine you are trying to sit on a chair.

63

## Addition & Subtraction Word Problems

1. Teddy was playing volleyball with his friend. Teddy scored 19 points and his friend scored 16 points. How many points did they score in total?

2. A cafe had 86 brownies. If they sold 54 of them, how many brownies would they have left?

   A. 38
   B. 36
   C. 34
   D. 32

3. Mary had 86 dollars saved up. After doing some chores her mother gave her another 26 dollars. How much money does she have in total?

   A. 92
   B. 102
   C. 112
   D. 122

4. Julie has 19 dolls. Her sister, Trish, has 38 dolls. How many dolls do they have in total?

   A. 53
   B. 57
   C. 68
   D. 59

5. Sean collected 156 baseball cards. He gave 42 of them to his friend. How many baseball cards does he have now?

   A. 116
   B. 114
   C. 112
   D. 110

6. A grocery store had 64 packs of regular butter and 28 packs of diet butter. How many packs of butter did they have in total?

7. While playing a computer game Vince had 73 points. If he scored another 16 points, how many points would Vince have in total?

8. Jake had 17 books in his bedroom. He had another 7 books in his locker. How many books did he have in total?

9. Dilan bought 3 T-shirts that cost $14 each. He gave the cashier $60. How much change should Dilan get?

10. A store had 46 cakes with jam and 32 chocolate cakes in the morning. How many cakes did the store have in total?

11. Dustin had 64 DS games and his friend had 57 games. How many DS games did they have in total?

    A. 101
    B. 111
    C. 121
    D. 131

12. A store had 564 cans of paint. They sold 60 cans of paint on Tuesday and 14 on Wednesday. How many cans of paint did the store have left?

    A. 502
    B. 498
    C. 492
    D. 490

**13.** Amy took **65** marbles from her box. Now she has **24** marbles in her box. How many marbles were originally in there?

**14.** For a birthday party, Mary had **67** balloons, and gave away **28** balloons. How many balloons does Mary have left?

**15.** In the first half of a lesson Christie solved **24** problems. In the second half she solved **18** problems. How many problems did she solve in total?

**16.** There were **468** buckets of popcorn in the movie theater. If they sold **142** buckets before the film started and **114** after the film started, how many buckets do they still have to sell?

**A.** 256
**B.** 234
**C.** 212
**D.** 188

**17.** While building a house, Billy used **945** boards. If he used **315** boards on the first floor and **420** on the roof, how many boards did Billy use in other places?

**A.** 250
**B.** 210
**C.** 200
**D.** 180

# FITNESS

Please be aware of your environment and be safe at all times. If you cannot do an exercise, just try your best.

Repeat these **exercises 3 ROUNDS**

**1 - Bend forward:** 10 times. Note: try to touch your feet. Make sure to keep your back straight and if needed you can bend your knees.

**2 - Lunges:** 3 times to each leg. Note: Use your body weight or books as weight to do leg lunges.

**3 - Plank:** 6 sec.

**4 - Abs:** 10 times

## Adding & Subtracting within 20

**1.** What is 14 + 5?

_____

**2.** Add.

_____

**3.** Solve 16 - 9.

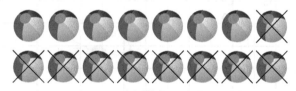

_____

**4.** What is?

_____

**5.** What is?

13 - 7 _____
15 - 0 _____
14 - 9 _____
12 - 5 _____

**6.** Solve 11 + 8.

_____

**7.** Find 4 + 16.

_____

**8.** Which sum is the least?

   **A.** 5 + 11
   **B.** 8 + 7
   **C.** 4 + 12
   **D.** 3 + 15

**9.** Add 7 to 9.

_____

**10.** What is the missing number?

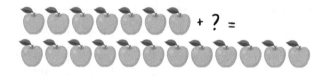 + ? =

_____

**11.** What is the missing number in the following equation?

8 + _____ = 14

_____

**12.** What is 20 - 12?

_____

**13.** Subtract 19 - 11.

_____

**14.** What is the missing number in the following equation?

5 + _____ = 17

_____

**15.** Calculate 14 - 8.

_____

**16.** What is 7 subtracted from 15?

_____

**17.** Find.

18 - 9 _____
17 - 6 _____
19 - 17 _____
15 - 8 _____

**18.** What is the missing number in the following equation?

11 - _____ = 9

_____

**19.** What is 8 subtracted from 17?

_____

**20.** Subtract nineteen from twenty.

_____

# FITNESS

Please be aware of your environment and be safe at all times. If you cannot do an exercise, just try your best.

Repeat these **exercises 3 ROUNDS**

**2 - Chair:** 10 sec.
Note: sit on an imaginary chair, keep your back straight.

**1 - High Plank:** 6 sec.

**4 - Abs:** 10 times

**3 - Waist Hooping:** 10 times. Note: if you do not have a hoop, pretend you have an imaginary hoop and rotate your hips 10 times.

## Even & Odd Numbers

1. Circle the odd numbers.

   5, 8, 1, 3, 6, 4

2. Which even number comes next?

   22, 24, 26, ﹏﹏

3. Is the number of leaves even or odd?

   Even
   Odd

4. Is the number of squares even or odd?

   Even
   Odd

5. Select the even numbers on the number line.

   ← 33  34  35  36  37  38  39 →

6. Circle the even numbers.

   12, 21, 17, 14, 6, 9

7. Which of the following numbers are odd?

   26, 33, 62, 88, 77, 44

8. Which odd number comes next?

   113, 115, 117, ﹏﹏

9. Select the odd numbers on the number line.

   ← 220  221  222  223  224  225  226 →

10. Is 111 even or odd?

11. Determine if the number of shapes is even or odd.

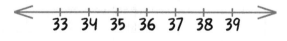

    Even
    Odd

12. Is 426 even or odd?

13. Which sum is odd?

    A. 12 + 36
    B. 44 + 33
    C. 13 + 17
    D. 41 + 61

14. Select the even numbers on the number line.

    ← 452  453  454  455  456  457  458 →

**15.** Is the number of stars even or odd?

Even

Odd

**16.** Circle the odd numbers.

56, 31, 22, 34, 75, 81

**17.** Which even number comes next?

142, 144, 146, _____

**18.** Choose the line which contains ONLY odd numbers.

**A.** 32, 11, 76, 12, 27
**B.** 3, 118, 9, 99, 54
**C.** 47, 171, 59, 63, 85
**D.** 86, 56, 129 ,443, 7

**19.** Which of the following numbers are even?

1, 658, 39, 73, 28, 96

**20.** Which subtraction problem gives an odd answer?

**A.** 17 - 5
**B.** 65 - 3
**C.** 67 - 25
**D.** 86 - 23

YOGA

Please be aware of your environment and be safe at all times. If you cannot do an exercise, just try your best.

**1 - Down Dog:** 10 sec.

**2 - Bend Down:** 10 sec.

**3 - Chair:** 10 sec.

**4 - Child Pose:** 20 sec.

**5 - Shavasana:** as long as you can. Note: think of happy moments and relax your mind.

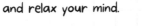

# EXPERIMENT

## Plants vs. Animals

*In our first two experiments, we saw how **plants** and **animals** work together to create new plants. This week, we'll be backing up a little and looking at some different kinds of plants and animals to compare their similarities and differences.*

*Although plants and animals are both **alive** and interact with each other often, there are several main differences between them. For example, animals tend to be able to move around and interact with the world through their senses (sight, hearing, touch, etc.). Plants, on the other hand, are rooted in one place and can't see, hear, or smell in the way that animals do.*

### Materials:

- Index cards
- Art supplies (markers, colored pencils, etc.)
- An adult
- An encyclopedia or internet access for research
- 2 pieces of plain printer paper

### Procedure:

1. At the top of one of your pieces of printer paper, write "**ANIMALS.**" Beneath that, it might be helpful to write:

   a. They can **move** around

   b. They can **see, hear, or smell things**

   c. They create and raise **babies**

2. At the top of the other piece of printer paper, write "**PLANTS.**" Beneath that, it might be helpful to write:

   a. They are rooted in **one place**

   b. They do **not** have senses like animals (can't see, smell, etc.)

   c. They create **flowers and/or fruit** to reproduce

3. Grab 8 index cards. On the top line of each card, write one of the following names: Goat, Spider Mum, Venus Fly Trap, Giant Sequoia, Platypus, Ghost Orchid, Arctic Fox, Monarch Butterfly

4. Get some help from an adult and look up each of those plants or animals using an encyclopedia or the internet. On each index card, write **3-5** facts about the plant or animal whose name is on there. Then, on the other side of the index card, use your art supplies to draw a picture of each one.

5. Once your index cards are completed, lay your cards out in a row, with either the facts side or the picture side facing up, and look at your pieces of printer paper. Sort your index cards by placing the ones that represent animals on the **ANIMALS** sheet and the ones that represent plants on the **PLANTS** sheet.

6. After you've sorted the cards you created, clean up your art supplies and think about other plants and animals you can identify.

**Follow-Up Questions:**

1. What was your **favorite** fact that you learned about a plant or animal in this activity?

_____

_____

_____

2. How is the Venus Fly Trap different from our typical ideas about **plants**?

_____

_____

_____

# YOGA

Please be aware of your environment and be safe at all times. If you cannot do an exercise, just try your best.

**1 - Tree Pose:** Stay as long as possible. Note: do on one leg then on another.

**2 - Down Dog:** 10 sec.

**3 - Stretching:** Stay as long as possible. Note: do on one leg then on another.

**5 - Book Pose:** 6 sec. Note: Keep your core tight. Legs should be across from your eyes.

**6 - Shavasana:** 5 min. Note: this pose is very important and provides you with long term benefits. Try not to skip this. Close your eyes and imagine who you want to be and what your goals are! Always think happy thoughts.

**4 - Lower Plank:** 6 sec. Note: Keep your back straight and body tight.

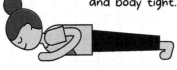

**Task:** Which route (Route 1, 2 or 3) should you take to end up at the top left corner? Color in the path!

1    2    3

# APRIL
# WEEK 4

April is the fourth month of the year and has 30 days. April is named after the Greek goddess of love, Aphrodite.

## Introductions

When we talked about **summaries** a few weeks ago, we said that two of the most important places to look when you're trying to access the main ideas of a text are the very **beginning** and the very **end**. That's because those are two places where authors try to present their ideas in a very basic, easy-to-understand way for the reader. This week, we'll be focusing on the very **beginnings** of things.

The beginning of an informational text is often known as an **introduction**. **Introductions** generally have three main purposes: to **tell the reader the main idea or topic** they're going to read about, to **get them interested in or excited about it,** and to **preview some of the different aspects** of the topic that are going to be discussed later in the text. Being a great writer means crafting introductions that set you and your reader up for clarity and success. Being a great reader means reading introductions closely to make sure you understand what's going on before you jump into the body of a text.

<u>What does an Introduction do?</u>

- **Tell the reader the main idea:** The beginning of an informational text should make it really clear what that text is going to be about.

  o For example, if your essay is about **snakes**, the topic of snakes should probably come up <u>in the very first sentence!</u>

- **Get them interested in or excited about that main idea:** For people to read something closely and really absorb it, they need to care. A good introduction shows readers how the topic is connected to their life or the world around them and makes them want to know more.

  o For example, if your essay is about **snakes**, tell the reader about how many snakes bite people each year or how many people keep snakes as pets.

- **Preview some different aspects of the text:** A good introduction is like a roadmap - it helps the reader understand exactly what journey they're going on. If something is a really big, important idea later in the essay, it should at least be mentioned at the beginning.

  o For example, if your essay is about **snakes**, tell the reader at the very beginning that they're going to learn about different kinds of snakes and how to recognize whether or not a snake is venomous.

- This will **grab their attention** and make them **keep reading** to get the information they want.

<u>What about Literary Texts?!</u>

Stories and other forms of literary texts don't necessarily have **introductions** in the way that informational texts do, but their opening chapters and paragraphs are still very important! When you read or watch the opening of a literary story, ask yourself...

- **Which characters** are presented first?

  o Who does the author want you thinking about at the beginning?

- **What kind of <u>place</u>** is being described in the opening pages?

  o Often, the first lines of description in a book or the first images on the screen in a movie are used to communicate to the audience the kind of world the story takes place in.

- **What happens first** in the story?

  o A lot of times, the very <u>first</u> thing that happens in a story predicts important things that happen later on!

## From "Blackfoot Lodge Tales"

### By George Bird Grinnell

### (Continued from Week 3's Passages)

In the night, when all were asleep, Old Man and the young man arose in their right shapes, and ate the meat. "You were right," said the young man; "this is surely the person who has hidden the buffalo from us." "Wait," said Old Man; and when they had finished eating, they changed themselves back into the stick and the dog.

In the morning the man sent his wife and son to dig roots, and the woman took the stick with her. The dog followed the little boy. Now, as they travelled along in search of roots, they came near a cave, and at its mouth stood a buffalo cow. Then the dog ran into the cave, and the stick, slipping from the woman's hand, followed, gliding along like a snake. In this cave they found all the buffalo and other game, and they began to drive them out; and soon the prairie was covered with buffalo and deer. Never before were seen so many.

Pretty soon the man came running up, and he said to his wife, "Who now drives out my animals?" and she replied, "The dog and the stick are now in there." "Did I not tell you," said he, "that those were not what they looked like? See now the trouble you have brought upon us," and he put an arrow on his bow and waited for them to come out. But they were cunning, for when the last animal—a big bull—was about to go out, the stick grasped him by the hair under his neck, and coiled up in it, and the dog held on by the hair beneath, until they were far out on the prairie, when they changed into their true shapes, and drove the buffalo toward camp.

1. **Underline** the part in the passage that shows where the buffalo were hidden.

2. **Why** would reading this passage be <u>confusing</u> if you hadn't read the Day 1 and Day 2 passages from Week 3?

_____

_____

_____

**3.** How do the "stick" and "dog" escape?

    **A.** They ride out on a bull

    **B.** They turn into their human forms and run away

    **C.** The dog carries the stick in its mouth

    **D.** The woman and the boy carry them back to the house

**4.** Based on the story, what does the word "cunning" (Paragraph 3) mean?

    **A.** Dumb

    **B.** Slow

    **C.** Smart

    **D.** Evil

**5.** Write a **summary** of 3-5 sentences that explains the story told between Week 3 Day 1, Week 3 Day 2, and this passage:

_____

_____

_____

_____

## Thinking About Introductions

**Directions:** Each question below is about **introductions!** Some of them ask you to create introductions for certain topics, while others are designed to make you <u>think</u> about how introductions can and should be used in writing. Remember, introductions should **get the reader's attention** and **reveal the main topic** without being too long or overly-detailed.

1. If you were sending a letter or email to someone you've never met before, which of these details would you want to **make sure was in the introduction?**

   **A.** A full autobiography

   **B.** A note thanking them for their time and stating that you are looking forward to hearing back

   **C.** A detailed list of all the different things you need to talk to them about

   **D.** A brief explanation of who you are

2. If someone wrote a paragraph about the <u>colors and symbols on the American flag</u>, which of these would be the **best introduction sentence?**

   **A.** The American flag features three colors and a few basic shapes.

   **B.** The American flag is flown all around our country and world.

   **C.** The American flag is very important.

   **D.** People should know more about the American flag.

3. If you wrote a <u>very long essay or book but</u> **didn't** <u>include an introduction,</u> which of these **problems** would someone have reading what you wrote?

   A. They wouldn't be able to read the rest of the information

   B. It would be difficult for them to predict where the essay or book was going

   C. They wouldn't be able to figure out your main idea

   D. They wouldn't know which of your ideas were most important at the end

4. If someone wrote a paragraph about the <u>dog show at the local fair,</u> which of these would be the **best introduction sentence?**

   A. There are many different kinds of dogs.

   B. Our local dog show brought out many of the area's cutest and coolest pets.

   C. There was a dog show recently.

   D. The local fair had its biggest and best weekend in years.

## FITNESS

Please be aware of your environment and be safe at all times. If you cannot do an exercise, just try your best.

Repeat these **exercises 3 ROUNDS**

**2 - Lunges:** 2 times to each leg.
Note: Use your body weight or books as weight to do leg lunges.

**1 - Abs:** 3 times

**4 - Run:** 50m
Note: Run 25 meters to one side and 25 meters back to the starting position.

**3 - Plank:** 6 sec.

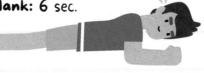

## From "Blackfoot Lodge Tales"
## By George Bird Grinnell

Once Old Man was fording a river, when the current carried him down stream, and he lost his weapons. He was very hungry, so he took the first wood he could find, and made a bow and arrows, and a handle for his knife and spear. When he had finished them, he started up a mountain. Pretty soon he saw a bear digging roots, and he thought he would have some fun, so he hid behind a log and called out, "No-tail animal, what are you doing?" The bear looked up, but, seeing no one, kept on digging.

Then Old Man called out again, "Hi! you dirt-eater!" and then he dodged back out of sight. Then the bear sat up again, and this time he saw Old Man and ran after him.

Old Man began shooting arrows at him, but the points only stuck in the skin, for the shafts were rotten and snapped off. Then he threw his spear, but that too was rotten, and broke. He tried to stab the bear, but his knife handle was also rotten and broke, so he turned and ran; and the bear pursued him. As he ran, he looked about for some weapon, but there was none, not even a rock. He called out to the animals to help him, but none came. His breath was almost gone, and the bear was very close to him, when he saw a bull's horn lying on the ground. He picked it up, placed it on his head, and, turning around, bellowed so loudly that the bear was scared and ran away.

1. **Underline** the detail from the <u>first</u> paragraph that explains why the events of the <u>third</u> paragraph are so complicated.

2. How could the Old Man have approached this situation differently to avoid needing to scare off the bear?

_____

_____

_____

_____

3. How does Old Man treat the bear?

   A. Kindly

   B. Respectfully

   C. Nicely

   D. Disrespectfully

4. Why are Old Man's weapons useless against the bear?

   A. The Old Man is too far away

   B. He is a bad warrior

   C. The weapons are made out of bad wood

   D. The bear is magical

5. How is the character of **Old Man** different in this story than he was in the longer story we read over the last three days of English activites?

_____

_____

_____

_____

## Crafting an Introduction

**Directions:** Read each short paragraph below, then <u>create an introduction sentence</u> that could go at the beginning of the paragraph. Be sure to be attention grabbing and introduce main ideas!

1. Pickup trucks have a cab, a place where the driver and passengers sit, and a bed. The bed is a long, flat storage area for cargo. The bed is what makes pickup trucks so useful. Sometimes, truck owners put a cover, cap, or lid on the bed to keep supplies inside and keep snow out. Unfortunately, trucks are also much heavier than regular cars, which means they burn a lot of gas.

**INTRODUCTION SENTENCE:**

_____

_____

_____

2. One of the most popular activities at the beach is swimming. Splashing around in the water is refreshing, especially on hot days. Many people also bring toys and games to the beach. Some people use buckets and shovels to build sand castles while others play catch with balls or flying discs. Other folks just like to lay around and get a tan, too.

**INTRODUCTION SENTENCE:**

_____

_____

_____

3. Even before he was the first president, George Washington was a very important American. He was a general during the Revolutionary War against England and a very respected man. After the war, people even wanted to make him king, but Washington knew that was a bad idea. He helped define what it meant to be president, and he was truly one of the most important figures in our nation's history.

**INTRODUCTION SENTENCE:**

_____

_____

_____

# FITNESS

Please be aware of your environment and be safe at all times. If you cannot do an exercise, just try your best.

Repeat these **exercises 3 ROUNDS**

**2 - Side Bending:** 5 times to each side. Note: try to touch your feet.

**3 - Tree Pose:** Stay as long as possible. Note: do the same with the other leg.

**1 - Squats: 5** times. Note: imagine you are trying to sit on a chair.

## Comparing two and three-digit numbers using comparison symbols (<, >, =)

1. Which symbol makes the statement true?

   45 ? 48

   A. >
   B. <
   C. =

2. Compare the numbers 63 and 72.

   ~~~~~~~~~~~~~~~~~~~~~~

3. Which number is greater, 48 or 37? Show your answer, using a comparison symbol.

   ~~~~~~~~~~~~~~~~~~~~~~

4. Which number is less, 253 or 323? Show your answer, using a comparison symbol.

   ~~~~~~~~~~~~~~~~~~~~~~

5. Show which sum is greater, using a comparison symbol. 36 + 28 and 42 + 19.

   ~~~~~~~~~~~~~~~~~~~~~~
   ~~~~~~~~~~~~~~~~~~~~~~

6. Which symbol makes the statement true?

   238 ? 216

   A. >
   B. <
   C. =

7. Which symbol makes the statement true?

   68 + 27 ? 34 + 61

   A. >
   B. <
   C. =

8. Which inequality symbol should be between the two stacks of books?

   A. >
   B. <
   C. =

9. Which expression is true?

   A. 68 < 63
   B. 72 > 89
   C. 112 > 119
   D. 49 < 51

10. Which number can be used to make the number sentence true?

    ~~~~~ < 532

    A. 529
    B. 541
    C. 603
    D. 556

11. Which symbol would make this inequality true?

    76 ~~~~~ 83

    A. >
    B. <
    C. =
    D. +

12. Compare the numbers 376 and 367, using a comparison symbol.

    ~~~~~~~~~~~~~~~~~~~~~~

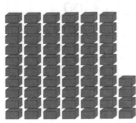
**13.** Compare the numbers of cubes.

**14.** Which expression is FALSE?

A. 57 < 65
B. 114 = 114
C. 187 > 193
D. 538 < 562

**15.** Compare the following numbers.

276 and 284 _____
609 and 596 _____
43 and 57 _____
337 and 373 _____

**16.** Compare the differences of 54 - 37 and 82 - 65

_____

_____

**17.** Compare fifty-one and eighty-nine. Show your answer using a comparison symbol.

_____

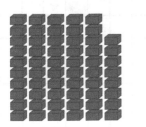 FITNESS

Please be aware of your environment and be safe at all times. If you cannot do an exercise, just try your best.

Repeat these **exercises 3 ROUNDS**

**1 - Bend forward:** 10 times.
Note: try to touch your feet. Make sure to keep your back straight and if needed you can bend your knees.

**2 - Lunges:** 3 times to each leg.
Note: Use your body weight or books as weight to do leg lunges.

**4 - Abs:** 10 times

**3 - Plank:** 6 sec.

## Mental math (Add 10 or 100 to any number)

**1.** Add 100 to 0.

~~~~~~~~~~~~~~~~~~~~~~~~~~~

**2.** What is 10 + 17?

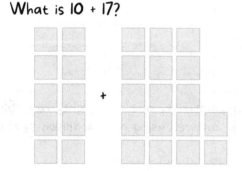

~~~~~~~~~~~~~~~~~~~~~~~~~~~

**3.** What is 19 added to 100?

~~~~~~~~~~~~~~~~~~~~~~~~~~~

**4.** Find.

$91 + 10 =$ ~~~~~~~~~~~~~~~~~~

$56 + 100 =$ ~~~~~~~~~~~~~~~~~

**5.** Calculate.

$40 + 10 =$ ~~~~~~~~~~~~~~~~~~

$100 + 72 =$ ~~~~~~~~~~~~~~~~~

**6.** Add 83 to 100.

~~~~~~~~~~~~~~~~~~~~~~~~~~~

**7.** What is the sum of 10 and 64?

~~~~~~~~~~~~~~~~~~~~~~~~~~~

**8.** Find.

$59 + 100 =$ ~~~~~~~~~~~~~~~~~

$48 + 100 =$ ~~~~~~~~~~~~~~~~~

$68 + 10 =$ ~~~~~~~~~~~~~~~~~~

$234 + 10 =$ ~~~~~~~~~~~~~~~~~

**9.** Solve:

$1 + 100 =$ ~~~~~~~~~~~~~~~~~~

$23 + 100 =$ ~~~~~~~~~~~~~~~~~

$420 + 10 =$ ~~~~~~~~~~~~~~~~~

$112 + 100 =$ ~~~~~~~~~~~~~~~~

**10.** What is 10+16?

~~~~~~~~~~~~~~~~~~~~~~~~~~~

**11.** Find:

$10 + 92 =$ ~~~~~~~~~~~~~~~~~~

$34 + 100 =$ ~~~~~~~~~~~~~~~~~

$27 + 10 =$ ~~~~~~~~~~~~~~~~~~

$100 + 406 =$ ~~~~~~~~~~~~~~~~

**12.** Add:

$10 + 0 =$ ~~~~~~~~~~~~~~~~~~~

$790 + 10 =$ ~~~~~~~~~~~~~~~~~

$651 + 100 =$ ~~~~~~~~~~~~~~~~

$100 + 8 =$ ~~~~~~~~~~~~~~~~~~

**13.** What are the sums of the following problems?

$10 + 2$ ~~~~~~~~~~~~~~~~~~~~~

$645 + 100$ ~~~~~~~~~~~~~~~~~~

$721 + 10$ ~~~~~~~~~~~~~~~~~~~

$100 + 900$ ~~~~~~~~~~~~~~~~~~

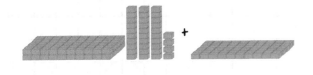

**14.** What is 234 + 100?

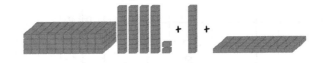

~~~~~~~~~~~~~~~~~~~~~~~~~~~~

**15.** What is the sum of the following problems?

307 + 10 ~~~~~~~~~~~~~~~~

214 + 100 ~~~~~~~~~~~~~~~~

10 + 835 ~~~~~~~~~~~~~~~~

100 + 461 ~~~~~~~~~~~~~~~~

**16.** Henry had **200** basketball cards, and Frank gifted him **10** of his basketball cards. How many basketball cards does Henry have now?

~~~~~~~~~~~~~~~~~~~~~~~~~~~~

**17.** Solve.

100 + 300 = ~~~~~~~~~~~~~~

534 + 10 = ~~~~~~~~~~~~~~

**18.** Add:

442 + 10 + 100 =

~~~~~~~~~~~~~~~~~~~~~~~~~~~~

**19.** What is?

100 + 37 ~~~~~~~~~~~~~~

10 + 68 ~~~~~~~~~~~~~~

308 + 100 ~~~~~~~~~~~~~~

290 + 10 ~~~~~~~~~~~~~~

# FITNESS

Please be aware of your environment and be safe at all times. If you cannot do an exercise, just try your best.

Repeat these **exercises 3 ROUNDS**

**2 - Chair:** 10 sec. Note: sit on an imaginary chair, keep your back straight.

**1 - High Plank:** 6 sec.

**4 - Abs:** 10 times

**3 - Waist Hooping:** 10 times. Note: if you do not have a hoop, pretend you have an imaginary hoop and rotate your hips 10 times.

## Problems involving addition/ subtraction/multiplication/ division with diagrams

1. Write an addition sentence based on the picture.

~~~~~~~~~~~~~~~~~~

2. Which addition statement describes the array?

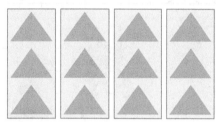

   A. 3 + 3
   B. 3 + 4
   C. 3 + 3 + 3 + 3
   D. 4 + 4

3. Use repeated addition to describe the array.

   5 + _____ + 5 + 5 + 5 = _____

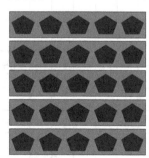

~~~~~~~~~~~~~~~~~~

4. Which picture shows 14 - 8?

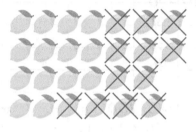

   A.
   B.
   C.
   D.

5. Write a subtraction sentence based on the picture.

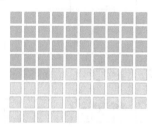

~~~~~~~~~~~~~~~~~~

6. Write an addition sentence based on the picture.

~~~~~~~~~~~~~~~~~~

7. Which expression describes the model?

   A. 4 + 6
   B. 4 x 6
   C. 4 + 4 + 4 + 4
   D. 6 + 6 + 6 + 6 + 6

8. Complete the multiplication sentence that describes the model below.

7 x _____ = 42

_____

9. Use two ways to describe the model. Fill in the blanks.

6 + _____ + 6 + _____ = 24

_____ x 4 = 24

10. Complete the multiplication sentence so it describes the array.

_____ x 6 = 24

_____

11. Write the array as an addition problem and solve.

_____

 **YOGA**

Please be aware of your environment and be safe at all times. If you cannot do an exercise, just try your best.

**1 - Down**
Dog: 10 sec.

**2 - Bend Down:** 10 sec.

**3 - Chair:** 10 sec.

**4 - Child Pose:** 20 sec.

**5 - Shavasana:** as long as you can. Note: think of happy moments and relax your mind.

## Vertebrates vs. Invertebrates

Last week, we explored the differences between plants and animals. This week, we're going to focus on **animals** and discover one of the most important distinctions between different kinds of animals.

**Vertebrates** are animals that have a spine or backbone. All people, birds, fish, and four-legged animals are vertebrates. Animals that don't have spines or backbones are known as **Invertebrates**. Bugs, spiders, and crabs are some of the most common invertebrates. Today, we'll create some models that will help us understand the structural difference between animals with and without backbones

### Materials:

- A paper plate
- Ribbon, cut into 8 equal pieces
- Art supplies (markers, colored pencils, etc.)
- A cardboard egg container (empty)
- String
- Scissors
- A hole punch (optional)
- An adult

### Procedure:

1. With help from an adult, cut the cardboard egg container apart into 12 individual pods.
2. With help from an adult, use scissors, the hole punch, or a sharp pencil to make a hole in the very middle of each egg pod, directly underneath where the egg would sit.
3. Once your 12 egg pods have been separated and pierced, line them up one behind the other as though you were making a **spine** out of egg pods.
4. Feed the string through each of the egg pods and tie a knot in each end, so you have 12 connected egg pods that can be flexed around. This represents a **snake** with a strong backbone.
5. Decorate your snake however you would like (you can add eyes, color, etc.)
6. Once your snake is completed, play around with it a little and see how it moves. How do the individual **vertebrae** (egg pods) in its spine work together?
7. With help from an adult, punch 4 holes on either side of the paper plate (this plate represents an **invertebrate** spider).

# EXPERIMENT

1. Thread ribbons through each hole on the plate and tie them off to create the spider's legs.
2. Decorate your spider however you would like (you can add eyes, color, etc.)
3. Once your spider is complete, play around with it a little and see how it moves differently from the snake. Think about how the snake's flexible spine and the spider's many legs accomplish the same job (moving around) in different ways.
4. Answer the questions below and clean up your art supplies.

## Follow-Up Questions:

1. What things can your **snake** do because of its spine that your **spider** can't do?

_____

_____

_____

2. Based on what you saw and read today, <u>why</u> do you think most bigger animals are **vertebrates?**

_____

_____

_____

 YOGA

Please be aware of your environment and be safe at all times. If you cannot do an exercise, just try your best.

**1 - Tree Pose:**
Stay as long as possible.
Note: do on one leg then on another.

**2 - Down Dog:**
10 sec.

**3 - Stretching:**
Stay as long as possible. Note: do on one leg then on another.

**4 - Lower Plank:** 6 sec.
Note: Keep your back straight and body tight.

**5 -Book Pose:** 6 sec.
Note: Keep your core tight. Legs should be across from your eyes.

**6 - Shavasana:** 5 min.
Note: this pose is very important and provides you with long term benefits. Try not to skip this. Close your eyes and imagine who you want to be and what your goals are! Always think happy thoughts.

**Task:** Fill in the crossword puzzle. Below are six pictures of animals. Write in their names (horizontally).

# MAY

# WEEK 5

**SPRING**

May is the 5th month of the year and has 31 days. We celebrate Memorial Day on the last Monday in May. We also have the famous Cinco de Mayo which falls on May 5th that celebrates Mexico's victory over France in the year 1862.

## Conclusions

When we talked about **summaries** a few weeks ago, we said that two of the most important places to look when you're trying to access the main ideas of a text are the very **beginning** and the very **end**. That's because those are two places where authors try to present their ideas in a very basic, easy-to-understand way for the reader. This week, we'll be focusing on the very **ends** of things.

The end of an informational text is often known as a **conclusion. Conclusions** generally have three main purposes: to **summarize the main ideas** of the text, to remind the reader **why the topic is important** and to **wrap things up in a memorable way** for the reader. Being a great writer means crafting conclusions that are clear and help the reader feel satisfied. Being a great reader means reading conclusions closely to make sure you followed the text in the way the author intended.

<u>What does a Conclusion do?</u>

- **Summarize the Main Ideas:** The longer a text is, the more likely a reader is to get lost or forget something they read earlier. That's why conclusions are so important!

    o Any points or ideas that the author thinks are **especially strong** should be summarized in the conclusion.

- **Remind the Reader Why the Topic was Important:** Like we said last week when we talked about introductions – people are more likely to enjoy a text if they understood how or why it is connected to their life.

    o A good conclusion reminds the reader **why they should care** in a way that makes them want to learn more and take the next step

- **Wrap Things Up in a Memorable Way:** Writers don't just want readers to get to the end of something and never think about it again – they want those readers to tell others about what they read and want to learn more about it.

    o The conclusion needs to wrap things up in a way that leaves the reader feeling excited and happy that they read the text.

## What about Literary Texts?!

Stories and other forms of literary texts don't necessarily have **conclusions** in the way that informational texts do, but their closing chapters and paragraphs are still very important! When you read or watch the ending of a literary story, ask yourself...

- **How did the story end?** What events take place in the final scenes? Were those events expected or unexpected?

- **Which characters achieved their goals?** Who in the story got what they wanted, and who didn't? Which characters were "winners" and "losers" at the end of the story?

- **Is the ending "certain?"** Have the characters fixed all the problems in their world, or is there room for a sequel?

## "The Fool & The Birch Tree"
## From *Russian Fairy Tales*
## By Ralston

In a certain country there once lived an old man who had three sons. Two of them had their wits about them, but the third was a fool. The old man died and his sons divided his property among themselves by lot. The sharp-witted ones got plenty of all sorts of good things, but nothing fell to the share of the Simpleton but one ox—and that such a skinny one!

Well, fair-time came round, and the clever brothers got ready to go and transact business. The Simpleton saw this, and said:

"I'll go, too, brothers, and take my ox for sale."

So he fastened a cord to the horn of the ox and drove it to the town. On his way he happened to pass through a forest, and in the forest there stood an old withered Birch-tree. Whenever the wind blew the Birch-tree creaked.

"What is the Birch creaking about?" thinks the Simpleton. "Surely it must be bargaining for my ox? Well," says he, "if you want to buy it, why buy it. I'm not against selling it. The price of the ox is twenty dollars. I can't take less. Out with the money!"

1. <u>Underline</u> another word from Paragraph 1 that means the same thing as "Simpleton."

2. How did the brother known as the "Simpleton" get his ox?

_____

_____

_____

**3.** Why does the Simpleton wind up in the forest?

    **A.** He wants to return the ox to nature

    **B.** He passes through the forest to take the ox to market

    **C.** He gets lost

    **D.** His brothers give him bad directions

**4.** What strange **mistake** does the Simpleton make at the <u>end</u> of the passage?

    **A.** He only gets an ox when his father dies

    **B.** He thinks the wind is his ox talking

    **C.** He thinks a tree wants to buy his ox

    **D.** He thinks the skinny ox is worth money

**5.** Based on how the passage ends, what do you predict will happen **next** in the story?

_____

_____

_____

_____

_____

## Thinking About Conclusions

**Directions:** Each question below is about **conclusions!** Some of them ask you to create conclusions for certain topics, while others are designed to make you think about how conclusions can and should be used in writing. Remember, conclusions should **review main ideas** and **remind the reader why they read** without being too long or overly-detailed.

1. If you had written an essay about the **whooping crane**, an endangered bird, which of these details would you want to **make sure was in the conclusion?**

   **A.** If people do not continue to help, whooping crane populations may shrink again.

   **B.** Whooping cranes have broad wings and long, bony legs.

   **C.** The sandhill crane is the only other crane species in North America.

   **D.** Whooping cranes live near the center of the North American continent.

2. If someone wrote a paragraph about the <u>colors and symbols on the American flag</u>, which of these would be the **best conclusion sentence?**

   **A.** The American flag features three colors and a few basic shapes.

   **B.** Some people believe a woman named Betsy Ross created the first flag.

   **C.** The American flag contains **50** stars.

   **D.** Our flag is so much more than just a piece of fabric.

3. If you wrote a <u>very long essay or book but</u> **didn't** include a conclusion, which of these **problems** would someone have reading what you wrote?

   A. They wouldn't be able to understand what they read before

   B. They wouldn't know who wrote the book or essay

   C. They might not recognize which points the author thought were most important.

   D. They wouldn't know what the book or essay was about

4. If someone wrote a paragraph about the <u>dog show at the local fair</u>, which of these would be the **best conclusion sentence?**

   A. Suzie Foster was the judge of the dog show.

   B. Even though only one dog could be champion, all the dogs were winners.

   C. All the dogs belonged to people who live in town.

   D. The fair ended on Sunday night.

# FITNESS

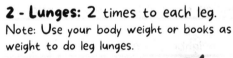

Please be aware of your environment and be safe at all times. If you cannot do an exercise, just try your best.

Repeat these
**exercises**
**3 ROUNDS**

**2 - Lunges:** 2 times to each leg.
Note: Use your body weight or books as weight to do leg lunges.

**1 - Abs:**
3 times

**4 - Run:** 50m
Note: Run **25** meters to one side and **25** meters back to the starting position.

**3 - Plank:** 6 sec.

## "The Fool & The Birch Tree"
## From Russian Fairy Tales
## By Ralston
## (Continued from Day 1's passage)

The Birch made no reply, only went on creaking. But the Simpleton fancied that it was asking for the ox on credit. "Very good," says he, "I'll wait till to-morrow!" He tied the ox to the Birch, took leave of the tree, and went home. Presently in came the clever brothers, and began questioning him:

"Well, Simpleton! sold your ox?"

"I've sold it."

"For how much?"

"For twenty dollars."

"Where's the money?"

"I haven't received the money yet. It was settled I should go for it to-morrow."

Early next morning the Simpleton got up, dressed himself, and went to the Birch-tree for his money. He reached the wood; there stood the Birch, waving in the wind, but the ox was not to be seen. During the night the wolves had eaten it.

"Now, then, neighbor!" he exclaimed, "pay me my money. You promised you'd pay me to-day."

The wind blew, the Birch creaked, and the Simpleton cried:

"What a liar you are! Yesterday you kept saying, 'I'll pay you to-morrow,' and now you make just the same promise. Well, so be it, I'll wait one day more, but not a bit longer. I want the money myself."

When he returned home, his brothers again questioned him closely:

"Have you got your money?"

"No, brothers; I've got to wait for my money again."

"Whom have you sold it to?"

"To the withered Birch-tree in the forest."

"Oh, what an idiot!"

1. **Underline** the part of the passage where the Simpleton begins to show frustration.

2. If you knew the Simpleton, how would you try to **explain this situation** or problem to him? What **advice** would you give?

_____

_____

_____

_____

3. Which word best describes what the Simpleton's brothers are doing throughout this passage?

   A. Stealing from him
   B. Teasing him
   C. Playing a prank on him
   D. Calling him a liar

4. What does the Simpleton tell the tree at the <u>end</u> of the passage?

   A. That he is going to cut it down
   B. That it's making him feel like an idiot
   C. That it is an idiot
   D. That it has one more day to pay him

5. Do you agree with the main character's brothers that he is an **idiot**? <u>Why</u> or why not?

_____

_____

_____

_____

## Crafting a Conclusion

**Directions:** Read each short paragraph below, then <u>create a conclusion sentence</u> that could go at the end of the paragraph. Be sure to **review main ideas** and help the reader understand why **they read something important.**

1. Yosemite National Park is located in California's Sierra Nevada mountains. The park contains numerous mountains, forests, and waterfalls. Each year, thousands of people travel from around the world to hike and camp in the Yosemite Valley. Along with Yellowstone and the Grand Canyon, Yosemite is considered one of the greatest and most beautiful National Parks.

**CONCLUSION SENTENCE:**

_____

_____

_____

2. Spencer has the coolest house. His parents have a pool with a retractable cover and a tennis court behind the garage. The entire basement of the house is a giant game room with ping pong and pool tables. The house is perfect for sleepovers.

**CONCLUSION SENTENCE:**

_____

_____

_____

3. My dad always complains that nobody ties up the trash bags right. He says you should only fill them three-quarters of the way so they're easy to tie. Everybody else in the family lets the bag get full. That means that trash always tries to pop out when we tie them shut. My dad is particular about the trash because he is in charge of the garage where it is stored, and he's the one who has to go to the dump every week.

**CONCLUSION SENTENCE:**

_____

_____

_____

# FITNESS

Please be aware of your environment and be safe at all times. If you cannot do an exercise, just try your best.

Repeat these **exercises 3 ROUNDS**

**2 - Side Bending:** 5 times to each side. Note: try to touch your feet.

**3 - Tree Pose:** Stay as long as possible. Note: do the same with the other leg.

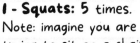

**1 - Squats: 5** times. Note: imagine you are trying to sit on a chair.

Measure the length of an object by selecting and using appropriate tools such as rulers, yardsticks, meter sticks, and measuring tapes.

1. Find the length of the pencil. Ruler is not drawn to scale.

A. 10 cm          C. 12 cm
B. 11 cm          D. 13 cm

2. What is the length of the book? Ruler is not drawn to scale.

A. 5 in          C. 7 in
B. 6 in          D. 8 in

3. Which is the best estimate for the length of a stadium?

A. 100 meters     C. 100 inches
B. 100 cm         D. 100 feet

4. What is the length of the bench? Ruler is not drawn to scale.

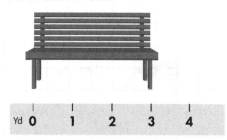

A. 1 yd          C. 3 yd
B. 2 yd          D. 4 yd

5. Find the length of the boat. Ruler is not drawn to scale.

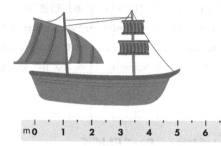

A. 3 m
B. 4 m
C. 5 m
D. 6 m

6. Move the ruler to measure the length of the line segment.

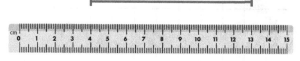

A. 13 cm
B. 12 cm
C. 10 cm
D. 9 cm

7. Find the length of the rectangle. Ruler is not drawn to scale.

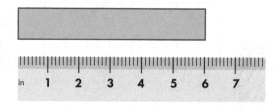

8. Which is the best estimate for the length of a car?

A. 15 centimeters
B. 15 inches
C. 15 feet
D. 15 yards

9. What is the length of the snake? Ruler is not drawn to scale.

10. Which is the best estimate for the length of a laptop?

   A. 20 inches
   B. 20 feet
   C. 20 yards
   D. 20 meters

**Measure the length of an object twice, using different units for the two measurements; describe how the two measurements relate to the size of the unit chosen.**

1. Measure the length of the block in inches and in centimeters.

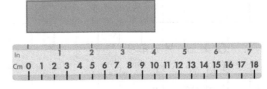

   A. 10 in or 4 cm
   B. 4 in or 10 cm
   C. 4 in or 11 cm
   D. 3 in or 10 cm

# FITNESS

Repeat these exercises **3 ROUNDS**

Please be aware of your environment and be safe at all times. If you cannot do an exercise, just try your best.

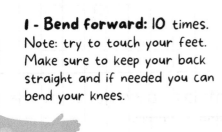

**1 - Bend forward:** 10 times.
Note: try to touch your feet. Make sure to keep your back straight and if needed you can bend your knees.

**2 - Lunges:** 3 times to each leg.
Note: Use your body weight or books as weight to do leg lunges.

**4 - Abs:** 10 times

**3 - Plank:** 6 sec.

Measure the length of an object twice, using different units for the two measurements; describe how the two measurements relate to the size of the unit chosen.

1. Measure the length of the rectangle in inches and in centimeters.

A. 10 in or 4 cm
B. 3 in or 5 cm
C. 2 in or 5 cm
D. 2 in or 4 cm

2. Measure the length of the ribbon in inches and in centimeters.

A. $5\frac{1}{2}$ in or 14 cm
B. 5 in or 15 cm
C. 5 in or 13 cm
D. 6 in or 15 cm

3. Measure the length of the bottle in inches and in centimeters.

A. 9 in or $3\frac{1}{2}$ cm
B. $3\frac{1}{2}$ in or 9 cm
C. 4 in or 10 cm
D. 3 in or 8 cm

4. Measure the length of the motorbike in meters and in yards.

A. 4 m or 4 yd
B. 4 m or 5 yd
C. $4\frac{1}{2}$ m or 4 yd
D. 4 m or $4\frac{1}{2}$ yd

5. Measure the length of the stripe in inches and in centimeters.

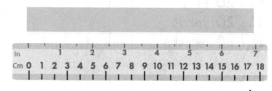

A. 6 in or 16 cm
B. 6 in or 17 cm
C. 7 in or $17\frac{1}{2}$ cm
D. $6\frac{1}{2}$ in or 4 cm

6. What are the measurements of the length of the table in feet and in yards?

7. Measure the length of the car in yards and in meters.

8. What are the measurements of the length of the board in feet and in yards?

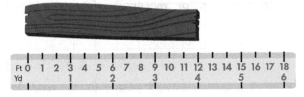

## Estimate lengths using units of inches, feet, centimeters, and meters.

1. Move the ruler to measure the length of the tulip to the nearest inch.

The tulip is about ———— inches long.

2. Measure the length of the telephone to the nearest centimeter.

The telephone is about ———— centimeters long.

3. What is the approximate length of a skateboard?

   A. 2 inches
   B. 2 feet
   C. 2 yards
   D. 2 meters

# FITNESS

Please be aware of your environment and be safe at all times. If you cannot do an exercise, just try your best.

Repeat these **exercises 3 ROUNDS**

**2 - Chair:** 10 sec.
Note: sit on an imaginary chair, keep your back straight.

**1 - High Plank:** 6 sec.

**4 - Abs:** 10 times

**3 - Waist Hooping:** 10 times. Note: if you do not have a hoop, pretend you have an imaginary hoop and rotate your hips 10 times.

## Estimate lengths using units of inches, feet, centimeters, and meters.

1. Move the ruler to measure the length of the broom to the nearest yard.

The broom is about _____ yards long.

2. The length of a hairbrush is about 25 _____. Choose 'inches', 'feet', 'centimeters', or 'meters' to fill in the blank.

3. Move the ruler to measure the length of the rope to the nearest foot.

The rope is about _____ feet long.

4. The length of a baguette is about 2 _____. Choose 'inches', 'feet', 'centimeters,' or 'meters' to fill in the blank.

5. What is the approximate length of a room?

   **A.** 7 centimeters    **C.** 7 inches
   **B.** 7 decimeters    **D.** 7 yards

6. Measure the length of the marker to the nearest centimeter.

The marker is about _____ centimeters long.

7. The height of a door is about 80 _____. Choose 'inches', 'feet', 'centimeters', or 'meters' to fill in the blank.

## Measure to determine how much longer one object is than another, expressing the length difference in terms of a standard length unit.

1. How much longer is the bracelet than the barrette (in inches)?

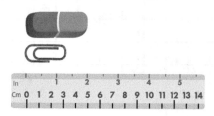

   **A.** 2 in    **C.** 4 in
   **B.** 3 in    **D.** 5 in

2. How much longer is the eraser than the paperclip (in centimeters)?

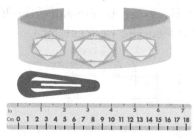

   **A.** 2 cm    **C.** 4 cm
   **B.** 3 cm    **D.** 5 cm

3. How much longer is A than B (in inches)?

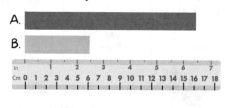

**4.** How much shorter is the couch than the ladder (in meters)?

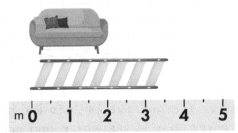

**A.** 1 m

**B.** $1\frac{1}{2}$ m

**C.** 2 m

**D.** $2\frac{1}{2}$ m

**5.** How much shorter is B than A (in centimeters)?

**6.** How much shorter is the boot than the pillow (in inches)?

**A.** 7 in

**B.** 8 in

**C.** 9 in

**D.** 10 in

**7.** How much longer is A than B (in inches)?

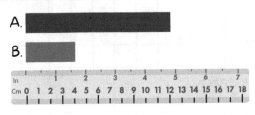

# YOGA

Please be aware of your environment and be safe at all times. If you cannot do an exercise, just try your best.

**1 - Down Dog:** 10 sec.

**2 - Bend Down:** 10 sec.

**3 - Chair:** 10 sec.

**4 - Child Pose:** 20 sec.

**5 - Shavasana:** as long as you can. Note: think of happy moments and relax your mind.

## Mammals, Fish, Reptiles, and Amphibians

Last week, we defined the term **vertebrate** as meaning an animal with a spine or backbone (like our model snake). This week, we'll be looking at some of the different ways we classify **vertebrates**. Specifically, we'll be looking at four categories: mammals, fish, reptiles, and amphibians.

**Mammals** (like humans) are vertebrates that have hair or fur and give birth to live babies, who are fed milk. **Fish** are vertebrates that live their entire lives in the water and breathe oxygen using gills. **Reptiles** are cold-blooded vertebrates with rough, dry scales that lay eggs. **Amphibians** are cold-blooded vertebrates with smooth or slimy skin that lay eggs.

### Materials:

- 4 pieces of plain printer paper
- Index cards
- Art supplies (markers, colored pencils, etc.)
- An adult
- An encyclopedia or internet access for research

### Procedure:

1. At the top of one of your pieces of printer paper, write "**MAMMALS.**" Beneath that, it might be helpful to write:
   a. They have hair or **fur**
   b. They give birth to live **babies** who they feed **milk**

2. At the top of one of your pieces of printer paper, write "**FISH.**" Beneath that, it might be helpful to write:
   a. Live entirely in **water**
   b. Breathe using **gills**

3. At the top of one of your pieces of printer paper, write "**REPTILES.**" Beneath that, it might be helpful to write:
   a. Cold-blooded with rough, dry scales
   b. Lay eggs

4. At the top of the final piece of printer paper, write "**AMPHIBIANS.**" Beneath that, it might be helpful to write:
   a. Cold-blooded with smooth or slimy skin
   b. Lay eggs

5. Grab 9 index cards. On the top line of each card, write one of the following names: Mako Shark, Newt, Red-Eyed Tree Frog, Moose, Iguana, Desert Horned Lizard, Red-Eared Slider, Red Fox, Northern Pike, Largemouth Bass, Black Bear, and Spotted Salamander.

1. Get help from an adult and look up each of those animals using an encyclopedia or the internet. On each index card, write **3-5** facts about the vertebrate whose name is on there. Then, on the other side of the index card, use your art supplies to draw a picture of each one.

2. Once your index cards are completed, lay your cards out in a row, with either the facts side or the picture side facing up, and look at your pieces of printer paper. Sort your index cards by placing the ones that represent mammals on the **MAMMALS** sheet, the fish on the **FISH** sheet, and so on.

3. After you've sorted the cards you created, clean up your art supplies and think about mammals, fish, amphibians, and reptiles you know of!

## Follow-Up Questions:

1. Which of the four groups of vertebrates do you think is the most interesting or cool? <u>Why</u> is that your favorite?

_____

_____

_____

2. Which two groups of vertebrates seem the most alike or the most similar to each other? What traits do they share in common?

_____

_____

  **YOGA**

Please be aware of your environment and be safe at all times. If you cannot do an exercise, just try your best.

**1 - Tree Pose:** Stay as long as possible. Note: do on one leg then on another.

**2 - Down Dog:** 10 sec.

**3 - Stretching:** Stay as long as possible. Note: do on one leg then on another.

**5 - Book Pose:** 6 sec. Note: Keep your core tight. Legs should be across from your eyes.

**4 - Lower Plank:** 6 sec. Note: Keep your back straight and body tight.

**6 - Shavasana:** 5 min. Note: this pose is very important and provides you with long term benefits. Try not to skip this. Close your eyes and imagine who you want to be and what your goals are! Always think happy thoughts.

**Task:** Do you like water slides? Five people below are going down a water slide! Match the corresponding numbers with the letters.

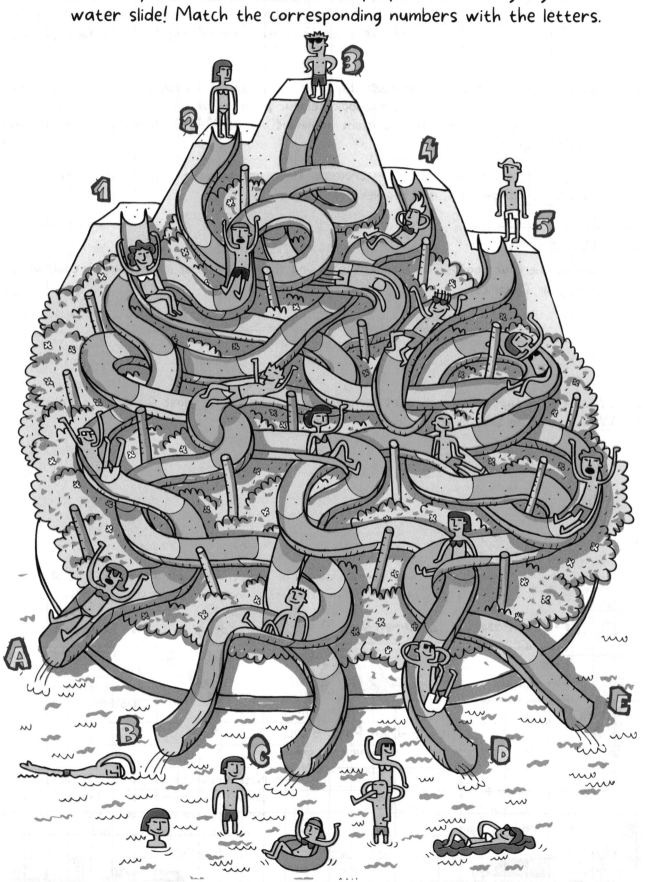

# JUNE
# WEEK 6

SUMMER

You must be excited during June since summer vacation starts at the end of the month! During the month of June, we have the longest daylight hours, and the weather is hot.

## Studying Characters' Actions

Over the last two weeks, we've focused on aspects of informational text (introductions and conclusions) that aren't always present in **literary texts**. This week, we'll focus on **literature and storytelling.** We recently talked about summarizing stories by thinking about their plot (the **sequence** of events that happen), but it's equally important to understand a story's characters and their actions!

When authors create characters, it's their responsibility to make those characters **interesting and memorable** by having them do exciting things and interacting with others in fun ways. For readers, those descriptions of specific characters and their actions help keep the story interesting and draw them into the world of the text.

As a growing reader, you need to start thinking about characters as you read! It's not enough to just focus on what happens in the story, you need to think about **what each character is doing!**

### Tips & Strategies for Studying Character Actions:

Here are three different strategies you should use as you read to make sure you're focusing on character-driven action, not just a passive understanding of "what happened in the story":

1. **Don't** just read what the characters do, **ask why they did those things!**

   - Just knowing what happened and what order things happened in isn't that interesting! Things are much more enjoyable when you start to ask **"What makes the characters tick?"**
   - Try to think about the story from **each character's perspective.** Why is each character involved in the story? What do they hope to accomplish? How are they working toward that goal?

     o Reading this way makes **everything** in the story more interesting and important!

2. Make note of how characters act when they **make decisions** or **run into obstacles**

   - Think about which characters **plan** or **think** out their actions and which characters **just do things** without thinking first

   - **At the end of the story,** check back to see if the characters have gotten better at these things!

     o Some characters **grow and change,** while others always stay the same!

1. Think about what each character's actions **say about their personalities or values**

   • Ask yourself, "If someone does that, what kind of person are they?"

   • Always ask yourself if a character's actions seem **consistent** with how they've acted to that point in the story

      o **For example,** is a character who seemed "good" suddenly doing "bad" things? Does a "bad" character still do good things sometimes? Are certain characters <u>always</u> "good" or <u>always</u> "bad"?

## "The Fool & The Birch Tree"

## From Russian *Fairy Tales*

## By Ralston

## (Continued from Week 5's passages)

On the third day the Simpleton took his hatchet and went to the forest. Arriving there, he demanded his money; but the Birch-tree only creaked and creaked. "No, no, neighbor!" says he. "If you're always going to treat me to promises, here'll be no getting anything out of you. I don't like such joking; I'll pay you out well for it!"

With that he pitched into it with his hatchet, so that its chips flew about in all directions. Now, in that Birch-tree there was a hollow, and in that hollow some robbers had hidden a pot full of gold. The tree split asunder, and the Simpleton caught sight of the gold. He took as much of it as his pockets would hold, and went home with it. There he showed his brothers what he had brought.

"Where did you get such a lot, Simpleton?" said they.

"A neighbor gave it to me for my ox. But this isn't anything like the whole of it; a good half of it I didn't bring home with me! Come along, brothers, let's get the rest!"

Well, they went into the forest, secured the money, and carried it home.

"Now mind, Simpleton," say the sensible brothers, "don't tell anyone that we've such a lot of gold."

"Never fear, I won't tell a soul!"

1. **Underline** the part of the story where it shows that the Simpleton was right that there was something special about the tree.

2. Who is the "neighbor" mentioned in Paragraph 1?

   **A.** The Simpleton
   **B.** The Simpleton's brother
   **C.** The Simpleton's father
   **D.** The tree

**3.** What does the Simpleton think when he finds the gold?

    **A.** That it is payment for the ox

    **B.** That the tree is magical

    **C.** That it was left there by leprechauns

    **D.** That it belonged to his father

**4.** Which of these describes the actions of the **brothers**?

    **A.** Brave

    **B.** Frustrated

    **C.** Greedy

    **D.** Stupid

**5. <u>Why</u>** do you think the brothers tell the Simpleton not to mention that they have so much gold?

_____

_____

_____

_____

_____

## Brainstorming Character Actions (Part 1)

**Directions:** Read each situation below and brainstorm at least **three different actions** the character in the description might display. Try to **be creative!**

1. LaTasha wants a new toy, but her parents say she hasn't done anything to earn it. What are **three different things** LaTasha could do to show her parents <u>she deserves the toy</u>?

   a. _____

   _____

   b. _____

   _____

   c. _____

   _____

2. Planktor is an evil criminal from another planet who wants to terrorize the people of Earth. What are **three different things** Planktor could do to show the people of Earth what a <u>scary, bad guy</u> he is?

   a. _____

   _____

   b. _____

   _____

   c. _____

   _____

**3.** Uncle Ted is a very clumsy guy who gets into funny situations. What are **three different things** Uncle Ted might do to show that he is <u>clumsy and funny</u>?

a. _____

_____

b. _____

_____

c. _____

_____

**FITNESS**

Please be aware of your environment and be safe at all times. If you cannot do an exercise, just try your best.

Repeat these **exercises 3 ROUNDS**

**1 - Abs:** 3 times

**2 - Lunges:** 2 times to each leg.
Note: Use your body weight or books as weight to do leg lunges.

**4 - Run:** 50m
Note: Run 25 meters to one side and **25** meters back to the starting position.

**3 - Plank:** 6 sec.

## "Ponies in Eastern Asia"

### From *Small Horses in Warfare*

### By Sir Walter Gilbey

The pony commonly used in China is bred in the northern part of the country. According to a writer in Baily's Magazine, immense droves of ponies run on the plains three or four hundred miles from Pekin, and the breeders bring them down every year for sale in the more populous districts. They average about 13.1 hands tall, and though in very wretched condition when brought to market, pick up rapidly on good food. They are usually short and deep in the barrel, have good legs and feet, and fairly good shoulders. Speed is not to be expected from their conformation; but they can carry heavy weights, are of robust constitution and possess great endurance.

The Burmese ponies are smaller than the Chinese, averaging about 12 hands 2 inches, a thirteen-hand pony being considered a big one. They are generally sturdy little beasts with good shoulders, excellent bone and very strong in the back; sound, hardy and enduring, capable of doing much continuous hard work under a heavy weight on indifferent food. Like the Chinese ponies, they are somewhat slow, but they are marvelous jumpers.

1. **Underline** the part of the passage where the author shares the name of another text he has read.

2. According to the author, what are some **advantages** (good qualities) of Chinese ponies?

   _____

   _____

3. Based on the passage, which of these is a way to measure height?

   **A.** Ponies
   **B.** Bailys
   **C.** Breeders
   **D.** Hands

4. According to the passage, what do Chinese and Burmese ponies have in common?

   **A.** They are both great jumpers
   **B.** They are both very fast
   **C.** They can both carry a lot of weight
   **D.** They both average 12 hands

5. Based on the **author's descriptions,** what <u>qualities</u> do you think he believes are important in a **pony**?

_____

_____

_____

_____

## Brainstorming Character Actions (Part 2)

**Directions:** Read each situation below and brainstorm at least **three different actions** the character in the description might display. Try to **be creative!**

1. Matt is an <u>honest</u> person who <u>treats everybody with respect</u>. What are **three different things** Matt could do to show that he is honest and respectful?

   a. _____

   _____

   b. _____

   _____

   c. _____

   _____

2. Kylie is very <u>jealous</u> of her sister Sammie. What are **three different things** Kylie could do that would show she is jealous of Sammie?

   a. _____

   _____

   b. _____

   _____

   c. _____

   _____

**3.** Pamela is <u>smart and brave</u>, and she always <u>stands up for what she believes in</u>. What are **three different things** Pamela could do to show that she is smart, brave, and driven?

a. _____

_____

b. _____

_____

c. _____

_____

# FITNESS

Please be aware of your environment and be safe at all times. If you cannot do an exercise, just try your best.

Repeat these **exercises 3 ROUNDS**

**2 - Side Bending:** 5 times to each side. Note: try to touch your feet.

**3 - Tree Pose:** Stay as long as possible. Note: do the same with the other leg.

**1 - Squats:** 5 times. Note: imagine you are trying to sit on a chair.

 **MATH**

## Time

**1.** Which clock shows three fifteen?

1  2  3  4

A. 1          C. 3
B. 2          D. 4

**2.** Which clock shows 9:45?

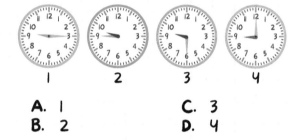

1  2  3  4

A. 1          C. 3
B. 2          D. 4

**3.** Look at the analog clock:

Which digital clock shows the same time?

2:30   6:10   5:10   1:30
1        2       3       4

A. 1          C. 3
B. 2          D. 4

**4.** What time does the clock show?

A. 9:10          C. 2:50
B. 10:10         D. 1:50

**5.** What time is shown?

A. 5:35          C. 6:25
B. 5:30          D. 7:25

**6.** Look at the digital clock:

Which analog clock shows the same time?

1  2  3  4

A. 1          C. 3
B. 2          D. 4

**7.** Draw the hour and minute hands on the clocks so they represent the time shown.

Answer:

**8.** What time does the clock show?

A. 2:40          C. 9:10
B. 8:10          D. 2:45

**9.** Which clock shows 4:05?

1    2    3    4

A. 1      C. 3
B. 2      D. 4

**10.** Look at the analog clock:

Which digital clock shows the same time?

**1:50**   **12:50**   **10:05**   **11:05**

1      2      3      4

A. 1      C. 3
B. 2      D. 4

**11.** Which clock shows eleven ten?

1    2    3    4

A. 1
B. 2
C. 3
D. 4

**12.** What time is shown?

A. 4:55
B. 4:00
C. 12:20
D. 11:20

---

 # FITNESS

Please be aware of your environment and be safe at all times. If you cannot do an exercise, just try your best.

Repeat these **exercises 3 ROUNDS**

**1 - Bend forward:** 10 times.
Note: try to touch your feet. Make sure to keep your back straight and if needed you can bend your knees.

**2 - Lunges:** 3 times to each leg.
Note: Use your body weight or books as weight to do leg lunges.

**4 - Abs:** 10 times

**3 - Plank:** 6 sec.

### Money

1. How much money is there in the picture?

   A. 55 ¢        C. 65 ¢
   B. 60 ¢        D. 66 ¢

2. If you have 2 dimes and three pennies how much money do you have?

3. Calculate the sum of the coins below.

4. Add $2 and 35 ¢ to $3 and 45 ¢.

   A. $5 and 65¢     C. $5 and 80¢
   B. $5 and 70¢     D. $6 and 5¢

5. Find:

    times 6 = _____

6. What is 43¢ added to 55¢?

7. What is $108 + $13?

8. Subtract 76¢ from $2.

   A. $1 and 24¢
   B. $1 and 25¢
   C. $1 and 26¢
   D. $1 and 34¢

9. What is $1 in cents?

10. Find:

    +

11. How much is this coin worth?

    A. 1 cent         C. 10 cents
    B. 5 cents        D. 25 cents

12. How much money is there? 1

**13.** Look at these coins:

Which group of coins shows the same amount?

A.

B.

C.

D.

**14.** Write the correct number.

6   = _____

**15.** What is the sum of 74¢ and 38¢?

**16.** What is the difference between $156 and $33?

# FITNESS

Please be aware of your environment and be safe at all times. If you cannot do an exercise, just try your best.

Repeat these **exercises 3 ROUNDS**

**2 - Chair:** 10 sec.
Note: sit on an imaginary chair, keep your back straight.

**1 - High Plank:** 6 sec.

**4 - Abs:** 10 times

**3 - Waist Hooping:** 10 times. Note: if you do not have a hoop, pretend you have an imaginary hoop and rotate your hips 10 times.

# MATH

### Measurement & Data

1. Measure the lengths of each ribbon (in centimeters) and then generate a line plot based on the information.

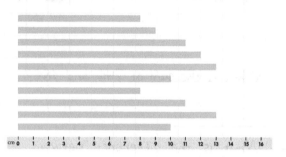

~~~~~~~~~~~~~~~~~~~~~~

2. Measure the lengths of each bar (in inches) and then generate a line plot based on the information.

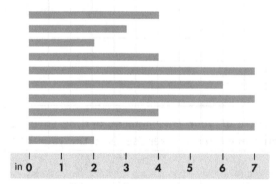

~~~~~~~~~~~~~~~~~~~~~~

**Use the line plot for questions 3 - 7.**
The lengths of some boards were measured. The line plot shows the number of boards for each measurement.

### Number of Boards for Each Length

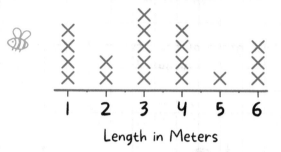

Length in Meters

3. How many boards measure **6** meters?

~~~~~~~~~~~~~~~~~~~~~~

4. How many boards measure **4** meters?

~~~~~~~~~~~~~~~~~~~~~~

5. There are **3** boards with the same measurement. What is the length?

~~~~~~~~~~~~~~~~~~~~~~

6. One more board was measured and added to the line plot. The board measured **3** meters. What is the new number of boards that measure **3** meters?

~~~~~~~~~~~~~~~~~~~~~~

7. One more board was measured and added to the line plot. The board measured **5** meters. What is the new number of boards that measure **5** meters?

~~~~~~~~~~~~~~~~~~~~~~

## Measurement & Data
## Tables & Graphs

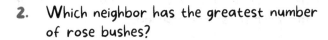

The neighbors counted the number of rose bushes in their gardens. The picture graph shows the number of rose bushes in each garden. Use the picture graph below to answer questions 1 - 5.

| Neighbors | Number of Rose Bushes |
|---|---|
| Mrs. Howard | 🌹🌹🌹🌹🌹 🌹🌹🌹 |
| Mrs. Peterson | 🌹🌹🌹 |
| Mrs. Watson | 🌹🌹🌹 🌹 |
| Mrs. Cooper | 🌹🌹🌹🌹 🌹🌹🌹🌹 |

1. How many rose bushes are in Mrs. Howard's garden?

2. Which neighbor has the greatest number of rose bushes?

3. How many rose bushes are in Mrs Watson's garden?

4. How many total rose bushes are in all gardens?

5. Which neighbor has the fewest number of rose bushes?

# YOGA

Please be aware of your environment and be safe at all times. If you cannot do an exercise, just try your best.

**1 - Down Dog:** 10 sec.

**2 - Bend Down:** 10 sec.

**3 - Chair:** 10 sec.

**4 - Child Pose:** 20 sec.

**5 - Shavasana:** as long as you can. Note: think of happy moments and relax your mind.

## Observing Animal Adaptations

*Over the last few weeks, we've begun to think about what makes different kinds of animals special or unique. Next, we'll be looking at the special skills, traits, or characteristics that make each animal well-suited for living in its environment. We call those skills, traits, and characteristics:* **adaptations**.

*An* **adaptation** *is a trait or skill animals have developed to make finding food, avoiding becoming other animals' food, or surviving in the area where they live much easier. For example, birds around the world grow different sizes and shapes of beaks depending on what kind of food they eat. Some birds that eat nuts grow huge, powerful cracking beaks while other birds that eat worms grow long, slender digging beaks.*

*Today, you'll look at three animals and study their* **adaptations!**

### Materials:

- 3 pieces of paper
- Art supplies (markers, colored pencils, etc.)
- An adult
- An encyclopedia or internet access for research

### Procedure:

1. At the top of one of your three pieces of paper, write **BUSH BABY**
2. At the top of one of your three pieces of paper, write **POLAR BEAR**
3. At the top of one of your three pieces of paper, write **COMMON SNIPE**
4. With the help of an adult, use an encyclopedia or the internet to research each of these three animals. Use one side of the note sheets you've created to find out...

   a. Where each animal lives (what kind of an environment is it)
   b. What each animal eats and how it gets its food
   c. What predators might want to eat that animal and how that animal avoids them
   d. What **adaptations** (physical traits or skills) does each animal have that helps them survive in their environment

5. Once you've gathered that information for all three animals, use your art supplies to draw a picture of each animal **in its environment** on the other side of the note sheet.
6. Once you've finished all three note sheets and pictures, review your work to think about how all three animals use different traits and adaptations to survive.
7. Answer the questions below and clean up your art supplies.

## Follow-Up Questions:

1. Based on what you saw in your research, **why** do you think polar bears are white?

_____

_____

_____

2. Choose **one** of the animals you looked at. What's one **more** adaptation you think would be useful for that animal? Why would that adaptation be helpful?

_____

_____

_____

# YOGA

Please be aware of your environment and be safe at all times. If you cannot do an exercise, just try your best.

**1 - Tree Pose:**
Stay as long as possible.
Note: do on one leg then on another.

**2 - Down Dog:**
10 sec.

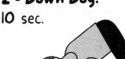

**3 - Stretching:**
Stay as long as possible. Note: do on one leg then on another.

**5 -Book Pose:** 6 sec.
Note: Keep your core tight. Legs should be across from your eyes.

**6 - Shavasana:** 5 min.
Note: this pose is very important and provides you with long term benefits. Try not to skip this. Close your eyes and imagine who you want to be and what your goals are! Always think happy thoughts.

**4 - Lower Plank:** 6 sec.
Note: Keep your back straight and body tight.

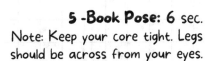

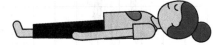

**Task:** Whoa! Looks like the giraffes have been tangled up. Match their necks (letters) to their body (numbers).

# JULY
# WEEK 7

Whooo! July... We celebrate Independence Day on July 4th all over the United States. On the very same date in the year 1776, United States declared independence from Britain.

## Using Illustrations

Many different kinds of books contain pictures. Some of the first books you read probably had a lot of pictures to make up for the fact that there weren't many words. Even as you start to read longer stories, some of them will still contain pictures known as **illustrations**. Illustrations **depict** (or show) certain events or ideas from a story to make the reading experience easier and more fun for the reader.

Now that you're becoming a more mature reader, though, you can't just look at illustrations - you have to think about them. Here are some strategies you can use to read both text and illustrations closely.

### Key Terms:

Illustration: A picture contained inside a book

Depict: To show something using a picture.

### Approaching Illustrations & Pictures in Text

- Start by looking at the illustration **on its own**

    o Wait until <u>later</u> to compare it to the written words on the page

- Start by noticing how many **characters** are in the picture

- Look at the **background** of the picture to learn more about the setting

    o What does the **world** of the story look like to the artist?

- Identify what **actions** are being <u>depicted</u> in the illustration

- Think about what the picture makes you **feel**.

    o What <u>emotions</u> does it trigger?

## Connecting Illustrations to Text

- After you've <u>looked at an illustration on its own</u> and read the text around it, think about how the two are **similar** or **different**
    o Do the characters in the illustration look the way they're described in the text?
    o Does the background and <u>setting</u> of the picture look similar to or different from what's being described in the text?
- **Ask yourself:** Does the illustration help you <u>understand or visualize</u> a part of the text that's **complicated** to describe or hard to understand?
- **Think:** Would you depict the action the same way, or <u>would you have done things much differently</u> if you were the illustrator?
- **Analyze:** Why do you think the author and illustrator decided that illustration was important to have in the text?

Once you can think about an illustration on its own and connect it to the text, you're on your way to getting much more out of the books you read!

## From "Alice's Adventures in Wonderland"
## By Lewis Carroll

The door led right into a large kitchen, which was full of smoke from one end to the other: the Duchess was sitting on a three-legged stool in the middle, nursing a baby, the cook was leaning over the fire, stirring a large cauldron which seemed to be full of soup.

"There's certainly too much pepper in that soup!" Alice said to herself, as well as she could for sneezing.

There was certainly too much of it in the air. Even the Duchess sneezed occasionally; and the baby was sneezing and howling alternately without a moment's pause. The only things in the kitchen that did not sneeze, were the cook, and a large cat which was sitting on the hearth and grinning from ear to ear.

"Please would you tell me," said Alice a little timidly, for she was not quite sure whether it was good manners for her to speak first, "why your cat grins like that?"

"It's a Cheshire cat," said the Duchess, "and that's why. Pig!"

She said the last word with such sudden violence that Alice quite jumped; but she saw in another moment that it was addressed to the baby, and not to her, so she took courage, and went on again:
"I didn't know that Cheshire cats always grinned; in fact, I didn't know that cats could grin."

"They all can," said the Duchess; "and most of 'em do."

"I don't know of any that do," Alice said very politely, feeling quite pleased to have got into a conversation.

1. **Circle** the names of all the characters in this passage once.

2. Which aspects of this scene **don't make sense** or seem like they're **confusing or weird on purpose?**

_____

_____

_____

3. According to **Alice**, what's wrong with the soup?

    **A.** It's too hot

    **B.** It's creating too much smoke

    **C.** It has too much salt in it

    **D.** It has too much pepper in it

4. How is **Alice** trying to act throughout the scene?

    **A.** Respectful

    **B.** Angry

    **C.** Aggressive

    **D.** Friendly

5. How does the **picture** add to the way you <u>think</u> or feel about the <u>characters</u> and <u>conversation</u> in this scene? What parts of the scene does the <u>artist</u> <u>seem focused on</u>?

_____

_____

_____

_____

## Decoding an Illustration

**Directions:** Look at the picture below and think about the **characters** and the **action** that are being portrayed. On the lines below the picture, write a short story (at least four sentences) that describes who the characters in the picture are and what they're doing.

(Note: This illustration comes from **R. Caldecott's First Collection of Pictures & Songs**)

# FITNESS

Repeat these
**exercises**
**3 ROUNDS**

Please be aware of your environment and be safe at all times. If you cannot do an exercise, just try your best.

**1 - Abs:**
3 times

**2 - Lunges:** 2 times to each leg.
Note: Use your body weight or books as weight to do leg lunges.

**3 - Plank:** 6 sec.

**4 - Run:** 50m
Note: Run 25 meters to one side and 25 meters back to the starting position.

## From "Alice's Adventures in Wonderland"
## By Lewis Carroll

The Cat only grinned when it saw Alice. It looked good-natured, she thought: still it had very long claws and a great many teeth, so she felt that it ought to be treated with respect.

"Cheshire Cat," she began, rather timidly, as she did not at all know whether it would like the name: however, it only grinned a little wider. "Come, it's pleased so far," thought Alice, and she went on. "Would you tell me, please, which way I ought to go from here?"
"That depends a good deal on where you want to get to," said the Cat.

"I don't much care where——" said Alice.

"Then it doesn't matter which way you go," said the Cat.

"—— so long as I get somewhere," Alice added as an explanation.

"Oh, you're sure to do that," said the Cat, "if you only walk long enough."

Alice felt that this could not be denied, so she tried another question. "What sort of people live about here?"

"In that direction," the Cat said, waving its right paw round, "lives a Hatter: and in that direction," waving the other paw, "lives a March Hare. Visit either you like: they're both mad."

"But I don't want to go among mad people," Alice remarked.

"Oh, you can't help that," said the Cat: "we're all mad here. I'm mad. You're mad."

"How do you know I'm mad?" said Alice.

"You must be," said the Cat, "or you wouldn't have come here."

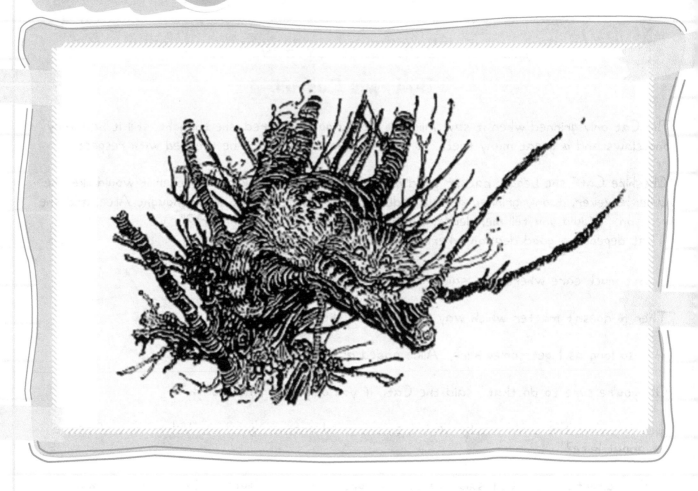

1. **Underline** the part of the text that shows why Alice feels she must **respect** the Cheshire Cat.

2. How would you describe the **picture** of the Cheshire Cat? What parts of the picture stand out to you?

_____

_____

_____

_____

3. What does Alice try to **ask** the Cheshire Cat?

   A. What she should eat
   B. What she should say
   C. Where she should go
   D. Who she should ask for help

4. Based on the passage, what do these characters mean when they use the word **"mad"**?

    **A.** Strange
    **B.** Angry
    **C.** Imaginary
    **D.** Fancy

5. Do you think the **Cheshire Cat** is a <u>funny</u> or <u>creepy</u> character? What makes you think that?

_____

_____

_____

_____

_____

# FITNESS

Please be aware of your environment and be safe at all times. If you cannot do an exercise, just try your best.

Repeat these **exercises 3 ROUNDS**

**2 - Side Bending:**
5 times to each side. Note: try to touch your feet.

**1 - Squats:** 5 times.
Note: imagine you are trying to sit on a chair.

**3 - Tree Pose:**
Stay as long as possible.
Note: do the same with the other leg.

## Depicting in a Story

**Directions:** Read the short story below and then **draw a picture in the box** that depicts an important moment in the story. Your illustration should include important **characters** and show a key **action** happening.

### The Owl & The Grasshopper
### By Aesop

An Owl, who was sitting in a hollow tree, dozing away a long summer afternoon, was much disturbed by a rogue of a Grasshopper, singing in the grass below.

So far from moving away at the request of the Owl, or keeping quiet, the Grasshopper sang all the more, saying that honest people got their sleep at night.

Fractions

**1.** What fraction of the shape is shaded?

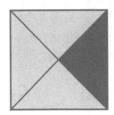

A. $\dfrac{1}{2}$    C. $\dfrac{2}{4}$

B. $\dfrac{1}{4}$    D. $\dfrac{3}{4}$

**2.** Which shape shows the fraction $\dfrac{3}{6}$?

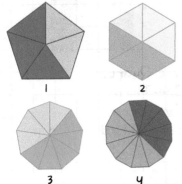

1    2

3    4

**3.** What fraction of the shapes are squares?

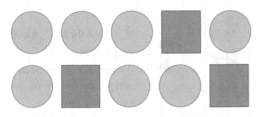

A. $\dfrac{3}{5}$    C. $\dfrac{7}{10}$

B. $\dfrac{3}{7}$    D. $\dfrac{3}{10}$

**4.** How many parts is the shape partitioned?

~~~~~~~~~~~~~~~~~~~~~~~~~~~~~~~~~~

**5.** What fraction of the shape is shaded?

A. $\dfrac{1}{3}$    C. $\dfrac{2}{5}$

B. $\dfrac{3}{5}$    D. $\dfrac{2}{3}$

**6.** Select the picture that shows equal parts?

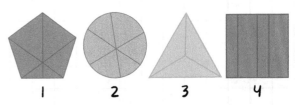

1    2    3    4

**7.** Which shape shows thirds?

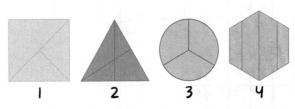

1    2    3    4

**8.** What fraction of the shape is shaded?

A. $\dfrac{5}{8}$    C. $\dfrac{5}{3}$

B. $\dfrac{3}{5}$    D. $\dfrac{8}{5}$

9. Determine which fraction best describes the shaded portion.

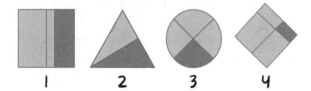

   A. One Quarter
   B. Two Quarters
   C. Three Quarters
   D. Four Quarters

10. Which shape shows fourths?

   1      2      3      4

11. What fraction of the shapes are circles?

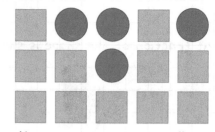

   A. $\dfrac{4}{11}$        C. $\dfrac{11}{4}$

   B. $\dfrac{11}{15}$       D. $\dfrac{4}{15}$

12. Determine which fraction best describes the shaded part.

   A. One Quarter
   B. One-Thirds
   C. Two-Thirds
   D. Three-Thirds

 **FITNESS**

Please be aware of your environment and be safe at all times. If you cannot do an exercise, just try your best.

Repeat these **exercises 3 ROUNDS**

**1 - Bend forward:** 10 times.
Note: try to touch your feet. Make sure to keep your back straight and if needed you can bend your knees.

**2 - Lunges:** 3 times to each leg.
Note: Use your body weight or books as weight to do leg lunges.

**3 - Plank:** 6 sec.

**4 - Abs:** 10 times

Understand a fraction as a number on the number line; represent fractions on a number line diagram.

**1.** Which fraction is missing from the number line?

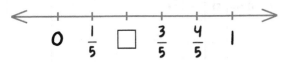

**2.** Which fraction represents one equal part of this number line?

A. $\frac{1}{5}$          C. $\frac{1}{7}$

B. $\frac{1}{6}$          D. $\frac{1}{8}$

**3.** Find the missing fraction on the number line.

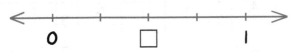

A. $\frac{1}{4}$          C. $\frac{2}{4}$

B. $\frac{1}{5}$          D. $\frac{2}{5}$

**4.** Where is the point on the number line?

A. $\frac{5}{9}$          C. $\frac{5}{8}$

B. $\frac{3}{8}$          D. $\frac{3}{9}$

**5.** Find the value of K.

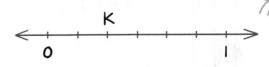

**6.** Which place on the number line is equal to the shaded part of the fraction represented in this picture?

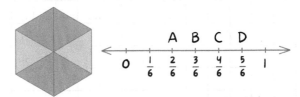

A. $\frac{2}{6}$          C. $\frac{4}{6}$

B. $\frac{3}{6}$          D. $\frac{5}{6}$

**7.** Find the missing fraction on the number line.

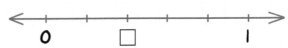

A. $\frac{2}{6}$          C. $\frac{2}{7}$

B. $\frac{2}{5}$          D. $\frac{2}{8}$

**8.** What fraction does the letter K represent on the number line?

**9.** Draw the dot at $\frac{3}{7}$ on the number line.

Answer:

147

**10.** Which place on the number line is equal to the fraction represented in this picture?

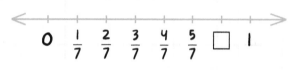

~~~~~~~~~~~~~~~~~~~~~~~~

**11.** Where is the point on the number line?

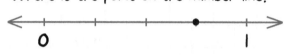

~~~~~~~~~~~~~~~~~~~~~~~~

**12.** Which fraction is missing from the number line?

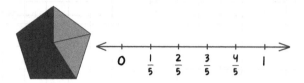

~~~~~~~~~~~~~~~~~~~~~~~~

**13.** Which fraction represents one equal part of this number line?

~~~~~~~~~~~~~~~~~~~~~~~~

**14.** Find the value of K.

~~~~~~~~~~~~~~~~~~~~~~~~

**15.** Which place on the number line is equal to the shaded part of the fraction represented in this picture?

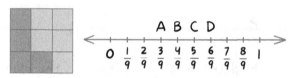

**A.** $\dfrac{3}{9}$      **C.** $\dfrac{5}{9}$

**B.** $\dfrac{4}{9}$      **D.** $\dfrac{6}{9}$

# FITNESS

Please be aware of your environment and be safe at all times. If you cannot do an exercise, just try your best.

Repeat these **exercises 3 ROUNDS**

**1 - High Plank:** 6 sec.

**2 - Chair:** 10 sec. Note: sit on an imaginary chair, keep your back straight.

**3 - Waist Hooping:** 10 times. Note: if you do not have a hoop, pretend you have an imaginary hoop and rotate your hips 10 times.

**4 - Abs:** 10 times

## Fractions & Number Lines

1. Put the dot at $\frac{1}{2}$ on the number line.

2. Determine which letter best shows the location of the fraction $\frac{1}{4}$.

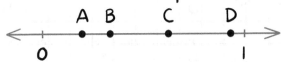

   A. A
   B. B
   C. C
   D. D

3. Which number line shows a marked segment with a length of $\frac{1}{6}$?

   A.

   B.

   C.

4. Which point is at $\frac{1}{3}$ on the number line?

   A. A
   B. B
   C. C
   D. D

5. Which point is at $\frac{1}{8}$ on the number line?

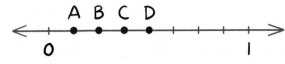

   A. A
   B. B
   C. C
   D. D

6. What fraction is located at Point A on the number line?

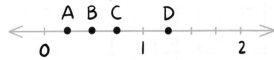

7. Determine which letter best shows the location of the fraction $\frac{1}{5}$.

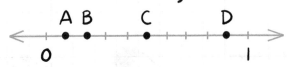

   A. A
   B. B
   C. C
   D. D

8. Which number line shows a marked segment with a length of $\frac{1}{7}$?

A.

B.

C.

9. What fraction does the number line show?

A. $\frac{1}{6}$     C. $\frac{1}{8}$

B. $\frac{1}{7}$     D. $\frac{1}{9}$

10. Partition into **5** equal pieces and label each partition.

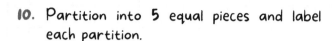

Answer:

11. Graph $\frac{1}{3}$ on the number line.

Answer:

12. What fraction does the letter on the number line represent?

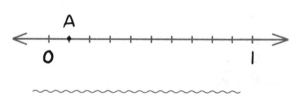

# YOGA

Please be aware of your environment and be safe at all times. If you cannot do an exercise, just try your best.

**1 - Down Dog:** 10 sec.

**2 - Bend Down:** 10 sec.

**3 - Chair:** 10 sec.

**4 - Child Pose:** 20 sec.

**5 - Shavasana:** as long as you can. Note: think of happy moments and relax your mind.

## Creating the Perfectly Adapted Animal

In Week 6's activity, you learned about the concept of **adaptations**: traits and skills that animals develop to make them really good at living and surviving in their environment. This week, we'll extend our thinking about adaptations by having you create your own original animal and designing it to live in a specific environment.

### Materials:

- One coin
- One six-sided die
- Art supplies (markers, colored pencils, etc.)
- Note paper
- Plain printer paper
- An encyclopedia or internet access for research

### Procedure:

1. At the top of a piece of notepaper, write "My Adapted Animal."

2. Flip your coin. If it lands on the heads side, write "Nocturnal" (which means your animal explores mostly during the night) on your notepaper. If the coin lands on the tails side, write "Diurnal" (which means your animal explores mostly during the day).

3. Roll your die. The number you roll will determine your animal's environment. Once you've rolled your environment, write it on your notepaper. If you roll a...

   a. **ONE**: Your animal is from the Mojave Desert
   b. **TWO**: Your animal is from the Olympic Forest in Washington
   c. **THREE**: Your animal lives in the Amazon Rainforest
   d. **FOUR**: Your animal lives in the Himalayan Mountains
   e. **FIVE**: Your animal lives in the foothills of Mount Fuji
   f. **SIX:** Your animal is from Madagascar

4. Once you know whether your animal is nocturnal or diurnal and what kind of environment it lives in, do a little **research** using your encyclopedia or the internet. A little help from an adult can go a long way here! Your goal is to figure out what that environment is like. Write down important facts or details about that environment on your note sheet.

5. After you've learned more about your environment, it's time to **brainstorm the perfect animal** to live there. You can create an entirely new creature from your imagination that's designed to live exactly in that place, or, if that seems too crazy, you can find an example of an animal that already thrives in that environment.

6. Using your art supplies and printer paper, draw a picture of the **perfectly adapted animal** to live in that environment. Label your picture so people can understand that adaptations. For example, if your animal has big ears, you can say, "Big ears for hearing predators at night."

7. Once your drawing is complete and your adaptations are fully explained, answer the questions below and clean up your art supplies.

## Follow-Up Questions:

1. Which adaptation do you think is the **most important** for your animal's survival? Why do you think that's so important?

_____

_____

_____

2. How does your animal obtain the food it needs?

_____

_____

_____

# YOGA

Please be aware of your environment and be safe at all times. If you cannot do an exercise, just try your best.

**1 - Tree Pose:** Stay as long as possible. Note: do on one leg then on another.

**2 - Down Dog:** 10 sec.

**3 - Stretching:** Stay as long as possible. Note: do on one leg then on another.

**4 - Lower Plank:** 6 sec. Note: Keep your back straight and body tight.

**5 - Book Pose:** 6 sec. Note: Keep your core tight. Legs should be across from your eyes.

**6 - Shavasana:** 5 min. Note: this pose is very important and provides you with long term benefits. Try not to skip this. Close your eyes and imagine who you want to be and what your goals are! Always think happy thoughts.

**Task:** Bob is out on a fishing expedition. He has five fishing rods, and it looks like they all hooked something! Match the fishing rods (numbers) to the object hooked (letters).

153

# AUGUST

## WEEK 8

August is the 8th month of the year and includes 31 days. The weather is hot, and it's the last month of summer vacation since school starts in September.

# OVERVIEW OF ENGLISH CONCEPTS

## Developing Text-Based Questions

Over the last seven weeks, you've done two Reading Comprehension exercises each week that involved looking at a passage and answering questions based on your reading. Many of those questions you've completed are what's known as **text-based questions**. As you start to read more complex books and texts, it's important to recognize what kind of questions are **text-based** and which aren't.

A **text-based question** is a question about a story that has a definite answer you can find by looking in the text. Basically, it's a question that you can only answer if you read the right part of the story and were paying attention. Let's look at some examples of text-based questions.

### Key Terms

Text-Based Question: A question about something you read that can be answered by finding the correct spot in the text

### Examples of Text-Based Questions:

- Where do the main characters live?
  - This question has a **definite answer** that can be found <u>in the text</u>
- What important item does Charlie find at the beginning of the story?
  - This question has a **definite answer** that can be found <u>in the text</u>
- Which character likes to play pranks on the others?
  - This question has a **definite answer** that can be found <u>in the text</u>

### Examples on Non-Text-Based Questions:

- How would you have reacted if you were in the same situation as the characters?

  - This question is **asking the reader for their thinking**, rather than asking them to refer to the text.

- How did that part of the story make you feel?

  - This question is **asking the reader for their thinking**. Even though they might talk about the text in their response, the <u>answer doesn't come from the text</u> – it comes from them!

- Which character is your favorite?

  o This question is **asking the reader for their thinking.** Even though they might give examples from the text in their response, the <u>answer doesn't come from the text</u> – it comes from them!

<u>**Answering Text-Based Questions**</u>

- Read the **wording of the question** carefully

  o A lot of times, you can figure out the **main words** in the question and think about where those words were used **in the text.**

  o Once you've found the spot those ideas are explored in, you just need to **read closely** to find the answer!

## From "Alice's Adventures in Wonderland"
## By Lewis Carroll

There was a table set out under a tree in front of the house, and the March Hare and the Hatter were having tea at it: a Dormouse was sitting between them, fast asleep, and the other two were using it as a cushion resting their elbows on it, and talking over its head. "Very uncomfortable for the Dormouse," thought Alice; "only as it's asleep, suppose it doesn't mind."

The table was a large one, but the three were all crowded together at one corner of it. "No room! No room!" they cried out when they saw Alice coming. "There's plenty of room!" said Alice frustratedly, and she sat down in a large arm-chair at one end of the table.

1. How many characters are at the "tea party" depicted in the scene?

_____

2. What are **two ways** the author shows that the Hatter and the Hare do not respect the Dormouse very much?

   o  _____

   o  _____

3. How are the **Hatter** and the **Hare** disrespectful or rude to Alice in the passage?

_____

_____

4. Based on all the passages from *Alice and Wonderland* that you've read so far, **who tried to warn Alice** about the way these characters would behave?

   **A.** The Duchess
   **B.** The Duchess' cook
   **C.** The Cheshire Cat
   **D.** The Dormouse

5. If you were in **Alice's position,** how would <u>you</u> feel about the March Hare and the Mad Hatter? **<u>What would you say to them</u>** when they told you there were no seats at the table?

_____

_____

_____

_____

_____

_____

## Thinking About Text-Based Questions

**Directions:** The questions below are all about the topic of **text-based question.** Read each question carefully and choose the best answer. Don't be in a rush to answer these, as the goal of the activity is to practice **thinking skills!**

1. How can you determine if a question is **text-based?**

   A. A text-based question can be answered using only information from the text.

   B. A text-based question forces you to think beyond the text.

   C. A text-based question involves asking the author to clarify confusing parts of a story.

   D. A text-based question is any question about a text.

2. Which of these is <u>not</u> a good strategy to help answer text-based questions?

   A. Look at the wording of the question and try to find similar words in the text.

   B. Create summaries of each section as you read to help you remember where main ideas are located in the text.

   C. Think about how you would write the text differently if you were the author.

   D. Reread the section of the text that contains ideas related to the question.

3. If you're reading a text that contains **pictures** or **illustrations**, which of these would be a good text-based question about the pictures?

   A. Who drew the pictures?

   B. Which sentence from the story is each illustration depicting?

   C. How could the pictures be improved to make them more artistic?

   D. Why did the author want to include pictures in the book?

4. Why would teachers ask their students **text-based questions** after they read a story?

   **A.** To force students to read slower.

   **B.** To check that students can find specific information in the text.

   **C.** To make sure everybody understood the general plot of the story.

   **D.** To help students memorize important facts from the story.

5. If you are reading an **informational text** whose goal is to <u>teach</u> you something, which of these is **not** a logical text-based question?

   **A.** What is the text attempting to teach?

   **B.** Does the text describe any steps or a sequence of actions I need to follow?

   **C.** How is this topic connected to the world around me?

   **D.** Is the teacher going to ask us about this?

# FITNESS

Please be aware of your environment and be safe at all times. If you cannot do an exercise, just try your best.

Repeat these **exercises 3 ROUNDS**

**2 - Lunges:** 2 times to each leg.
Note: Use your body weight or books as weight to do leg lunges.

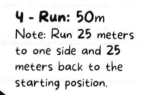

**4 - Run:** 50m
Note: Run 25 meters to one side and 25 meters back to the starting position.

**1 - Abs:** 3 times

**3 - Plank:** 6 sec.

## From "Alice's Adventures in Wonderland"
## By Lewis Carroll

"Get to your places!" shouted the Queen in a voice of thunder, and people began running about in all directions, tumbling up against each other; however, they got settled down in a minute or two, and the game began. Alice thought she had never seen such a curious croquet-ground in all her life; it was all very bumpy; the balls were live hedgehogs, the mallets live flamingoes, and the soldiers had to double themselves up and to stand upon their hands and feet, to make the arches.

The chief difficulty Alice found at first was in managing her flamingo; she succeeded in getting its body tucked away, comfortably enough, under her arm, with its legs hanging down, but generally, just as she had got its neck nicely straightened out, and was going to give the hedgehog a blow with its head, it would twist itself round and look up in her face, with such a puzzled expression that she could not help bursting out laughing: and when she had got its head down, and was going to begin again, it was very annoyed to find that the hedgehog had unrolled itself and was in the act of crawling away: besides all this, there was generally a ridge or a furrow in the way wherever she wanted to send the hedgehog to, and, as the doubled-up soldiers were always getting up and walking off to other parts of the ground, Alice soon came to the conclusion that it was a very difficult game indeed.

1. **Circle** the part of the story that explains what game the characters are playing in this scene.

2. Which of these objects does Alice have to hold to play the game?

   **A.** A hedgehog

   **B.** A flamingo

   **C.** A soldier

   **D.** The Queen

3. **What challenge** does the ball being a hedgehog present to the game?

_____

_____

161

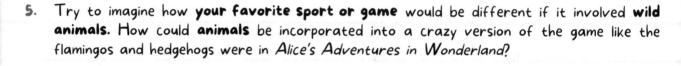

4. Which of these words best describes how Alice feels during this game?

    **A.** Frustrated

    **B.** Excited

    **C.** Competitive

    **D.** Angry

5. Try to imagine how **your favorite sport or game** would be different if it involved **wild animals.** How could **animals** be incorporated into a crazy version of the game like the flamingos and hedgehogs were in *Alice's Adventures in Wonderland?*

_____

_____

_____

_____

_____

## Creating Text-Based Questions

**Directions:** Read the short story below and create **two text-based questions** for another student to answer. Remember, your questions should **force the reader to look over the text again and focus on specific, clear ideas.** If you need some inspiration, look at the kinds of questions that have been part of the Reading Comprehension activities in this workbook!

### THE STAG AT THE LAKE

#### By Aesop

A STAG (male deer), one hot day, came to drink from a clear lake, and stopped to look at his own image in the water.

"How beautiful are my fine spreading horns!" said he. "How strong and graceful they are, branching from each side of my head! What a pity it is that my legs should be so thin and ugly!"

Just at this moment a lion came crashing through the forest and made ready to spring upon him. Away went the stag! and the legs that he had despised would soon have carried him out of danger; but when he came to the thick woods, his beautiful antlers, of which he had been so vain, caught in the branches and held him fast until the lion came up and seized him.

1. **Question 1:** _____

_____

_____

A. _____

B. _____

C. _____

D. _____

**Correct Answer:** _____

2. **Question 2:** _____

_____

_____

A. _____

_____

B. _____

_____

C. _____

_____

D. _____

_____

**Correct Answer:** _____

# FITNESS

Please be aware of your environment and be safe at all times. If you cannot do an exercise, just try your best.

Repeat these **exercises 3 ROUNDS**

**2 - Side Bending:** 5 times to each side. Note: try to touch your feet.

**3 - Tree Pose:** Stay as long as possible. Note: do the same with the other leg.

**1 - Squats:** 5 times. Note: imagine you are trying to sit on a chair.

Explain equivalence of fractions in special cases, and compare fractions by reasoning about their size.

1. Use the models to complete the equivalent fraction sentence. The shaded pieces in each model show parts of the whole.

$$\frac{2}{4} = \frac{?}{8}$$

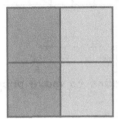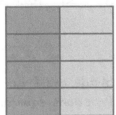

2. Use the model to complete the equivalent fraction sentence. The shaded pieces show parts of the whole.

$$\frac{?}{3} = \frac{?}{6}$$

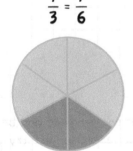

3. Which fraction is equivalent to $\frac{2}{4}$?

A. $\frac{3}{5}$  C. $\frac{1}{3}$

B. $\frac{4}{8}$  D. $\frac{5}{6}$

4. Find the missing number that makes these fractions equal:

$$\frac{?}{5} = \frac{6}{10}$$

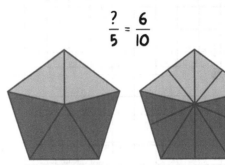

5. Choose the pair of fractions which are equivalent.

A. $\frac{2}{3}$ and $\frac{4}{6}$  C. $\frac{2}{4}$ and $\frac{1}{3}$

B. $\frac{1}{4}$ and $\frac{3}{8}$  D. $\frac{4}{6}$ and $\frac{5}{7}$

6. Which fraction is NOT equivalent to $\frac{1}{2}$?

A. $\frac{3}{6}$  C. $\frac{4}{5}$

B. $\frac{2}{4}$  D. $\frac{5}{10}$

7. Which pair of fractions is NOT equivalent.

A. $\frac{1}{2}$ and $\frac{4}{8}$  C. $\frac{2}{6}$ and $\frac{5}{10}$

B. $\frac{2}{5}$ and $\frac{4}{10}$  D. $\frac{3}{6}$ and $\frac{6}{12}$

8. Choose the fraction greater than $\frac{1}{2}$.

A. $\frac{2}{5}$

B. $\frac{4}{8}$

C. $\frac{6}{8}$

D. $\frac{1}{4}$

9. Color each pie that represents the fraction and fill in the box with <, >, or =.

$\frac{2}{3}$ ___ $\frac{4}{6}$

10. Represent the shaded parts as a fraction and compare using <, >, or =.

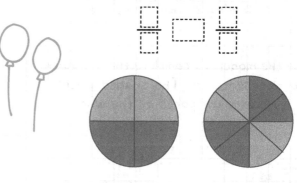

11. Shade the fraction bars to make proper fractions equivalent.

$\frac{1}{3} = \frac{3}{9}$

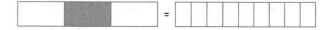

# FITNESS

Repeat these **exercises 3 ROUNDS**

Please be aware of your environment and be safe at all times. If you cannot do an exercise, just try your best.

**1 - Bend forward:** 10 times.
Note: try to touch your feet. Make sure to keep your back straight and if needed you can bend your knees.

**2 - Lunges:** 3 times to each leg.
Note: Use your body weight or books as weight to do leg lunges.

**3 - Plank:** 6 sec.

**4 - Abs:** 10 times

**Understand two fractions as equivalent (equal) if they are the same size, or the same point on a number line.**

1. Use the number lines to find a pair of equivalent fractions between 0 and 1.

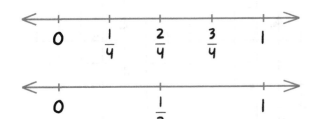

2. Are $\frac{4}{6}$ and $\frac{2}{3}$ equivalent fractions?

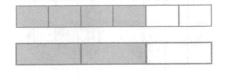

3. Write the equivalent fraction with a denominator of 8:

$$\frac{3}{4} = \frac{?}{8}$$

4. Which fraction is the lowest term of $\frac{4}{12}$?

A. $\frac{1}{12}$     C. $\frac{1}{3}$

B. $\frac{3}{8}$     D. $\frac{2}{6}$

5. Is $\frac{2}{5}$ equivalent to $\frac{1}{4}$?

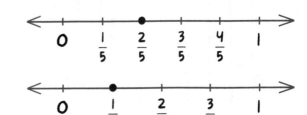

6. Put the missing number that makes these fractions equal:

$$\frac{5}{7} = \frac{10}{?}$$

7. Are $\frac{3}{8}$ and $\frac{2}{4}$ equivalent fractions?

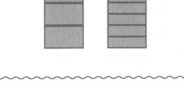

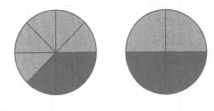

8. Use the number lines to find pairs of equivalent fractions between 0 and 1.

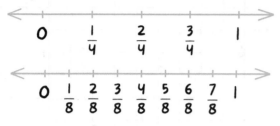

9. Write the equivalent proper fractions for the fraction models below.

Answer: ⬚/⬚  ⬚  ⬚/⬚

10. Use the number lines to determine a fraction which is equivalent to $\frac{2}{3}$.

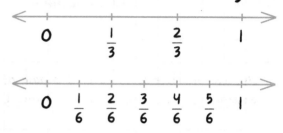

A. $\frac{3}{6}$   C. $\frac{5}{6}$

B. $\frac{4}{6}$   D. $\frac{6}{6}$

11. Put the missing number that makes these fractions equal:

$$\frac{?}{8} = \frac{10}{16}$$

# FITNESS

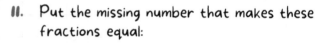

Please be aware of your environment and be safe at all times. If you cannot do an exercise, just try your best.

Repeat these **exercises 3 ROUNDS**

**2 - Chair:** 10 sec.
Note: sit on an imaginary chair, keep your back straight.

**1 - High Plank:** 6 sec.

**4 - Abs:** 10 times

**3 - Waist Hooping:** 10 times. Note: if you do not have a hoop, pretend you have an imaginary hoop and rotate your hips 10 times.

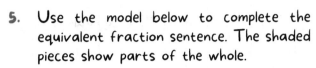

Recognize and generate simple equivalent fractions and explain why the fractions are equivalent.

1. Find a fraction equivalent to $\frac{3}{4}$.

   A. $\frac{4}{5}$     C. $\frac{6}{8}$

   B. $\frac{2}{3}$     D. $\frac{1}{2}$

2. Fill in the missing numbers.
   $$\frac{1}{3} = \frac{2}{?} = \frac{?}{12}$$

3. Write $\frac{6}{12}$ in lowest terms.

4. Find the value of n.
   $$\frac{5}{10} = \frac{n}{2}$$

   A. n = 1
   B. n = 2
   C. n = 3
   D. n = 4

5. Use the model below to complete the equivalent fraction sentence. The shaded pieces show parts of the whole.
   $$\frac{1}{?} = \frac{2}{?}$$

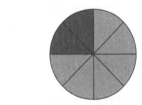

6. Which fraction is equivalent to $\frac{1}{3}$?

   A. $\frac{3}{8}$     C. $\frac{4}{9}$

   B. $\frac{5}{15}$     D. $\frac{2}{5}$

7. Which fraction is NOT equivalent to $\frac{1}{4}$?

   A. $\frac{2}{8}$     C. $\frac{3}{12}$

   B. $\frac{4}{16}$     D. $\frac{5}{25}$

8. Put the missing number that makes these fractions equal:
   $$\frac{2}{3} = \frac{?}{9}$$

9. Choose a pair of equivalent fractions.

   A. $\frac{1}{2}$ and $\frac{4}{6}$     C. $\frac{2}{3}$ and $\frac{4}{9}$

   B. $\frac{1}{4}$ and $\frac{3}{12}$     D. $\frac{3}{5}$ and $\frac{8}{10}$

10. Which fraction is NOT equivalent to $\frac{3}{6}$?

   A. $\frac{1}{2}$    C. $\frac{2}{4}$

   B. $\frac{9}{18}$    D. $\frac{4}{10}$

11. Write $\frac{4}{16}$ in lowest terms.

_____

12. Fill in the missing numbers.

$$\frac{2}{5} = \frac{?}{10} = \frac{8}{?} = \frac{?}{40}$$

_____

13. Put the missing number that makes these fractions equal:

$$\frac{?}{6} = \frac{8}{12}$$

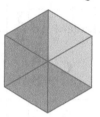 

~~~~~~~~~~~~~~~~~~~~~

14. Which fraction is equivalent to $\frac{4}{10}$?

   A. $\frac{1}{2}$    C. $\frac{2}{4}$

   B. $\frac{2}{3}$    D. $\frac{2}{5}$

Please be aware of your environment and be safe at all times. If you cannot do an exercise, just try your best.

**1 - Down Dog:** 10 sec.

**2 - Bend Down:** 10 sec.

**3 - Chair:** 10 sec.

**4 - Child Pose:** 20 sec.

**5 - Shavasana:** as long as you can. Note: think of happy moments and relax your mind.

# EXPERIMENT

## Observing Erosion

So far this summer, we've mostly focused on living things like **plants** and **animals**. Now, we're going to shift gears and talk about some natural forces and potential disasters.

*Erosion* is a natural process caused by <u>water, wind, and other natural factors</u> that cause land to weaken or wash away. Today, we'll be creating some erosion for you to observe firsthand!

### Materials:

- A small bag of sand
- Running water
- Two paper or plastic cups
- A shoebox
- A small electric fan (handheld is preferable)
- A plastic trash bag
- A safe place to experiment outdoors

### Procedure:

1. Bring all your materials outside and lay the plastic trash bag down on the ground to capture any sand that might blow around.

2. Pack one of your paper cups full of sand and add some water. Press the sand in tightly so that it will hold the shape of the cup (as if you were building a sand castle).

3. Place the sand "mountain" you've just created inside the shoebox (closer to one side is helpful). Be sure to remove the cup so that only the tiny sand mountain is in the box. (<u>An adult's help</u> can be very useful with this!)

4. Fill your other paper or plastic cup up with room temperature water from the sink. Dump that cup on the far side of the shoebox, away from your sand mountain.

5. <u>Gently</u> tip your shoebox back and forth so that the water can get under the bottom of the mountain. Notice what happens as the liquid water begins to interact with the sand mountain.

6. Turn on your handheld fan and hold it up next to your mountain. This represents wind. Observe what happens as you move your fan around the sand mountain and how things change as the mountain is exposed to more and more wind.

7. Using water and wind, see if you can make the sand mountain collapse or fall apart entirely!

8. Once your sand mountain has been destroyed, answer the questions below and then clean up your materials.

**Follow-Up Questions:**

1. Based on what you saw, how do wind and rain work together to erode land?

_____

_____

_____

2. For which people and animals is erosion potentially most dangerous?

_____

_____

_____

 YOGA

Please be aware of your environment and be safe at all times. If you cannot do an exercise, just try your best.

**1 - Tree Pose:** Stay as long as possible. Note: do on one leg then on another.

**2 - Down Dog:** 10 sec.

**3 - Stretching:** Stay as long as possible. Note: do on one leg then on another.

**5 -Book Pose:** 6 sec. Note: Keep your core tight. Legs should be across from your eyes.

**6 - Shavasana:** 5 min. Note: this pose is very important and provides you with long term benefits. Try not to skip this. Close your eyes and imagine who you want to be and what your goals are! Always think happy thoughts.

**4 - Lower Plank:** 6 sec. Note: Keep your back straight and body tight.

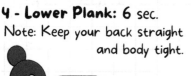

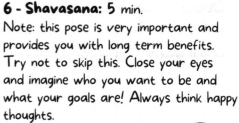

**Task:** Minnie the ant needs to get to the other side where her home is. Color in the correct path so Minnie can get home.

# SEPTEMBER

## WEEK 9

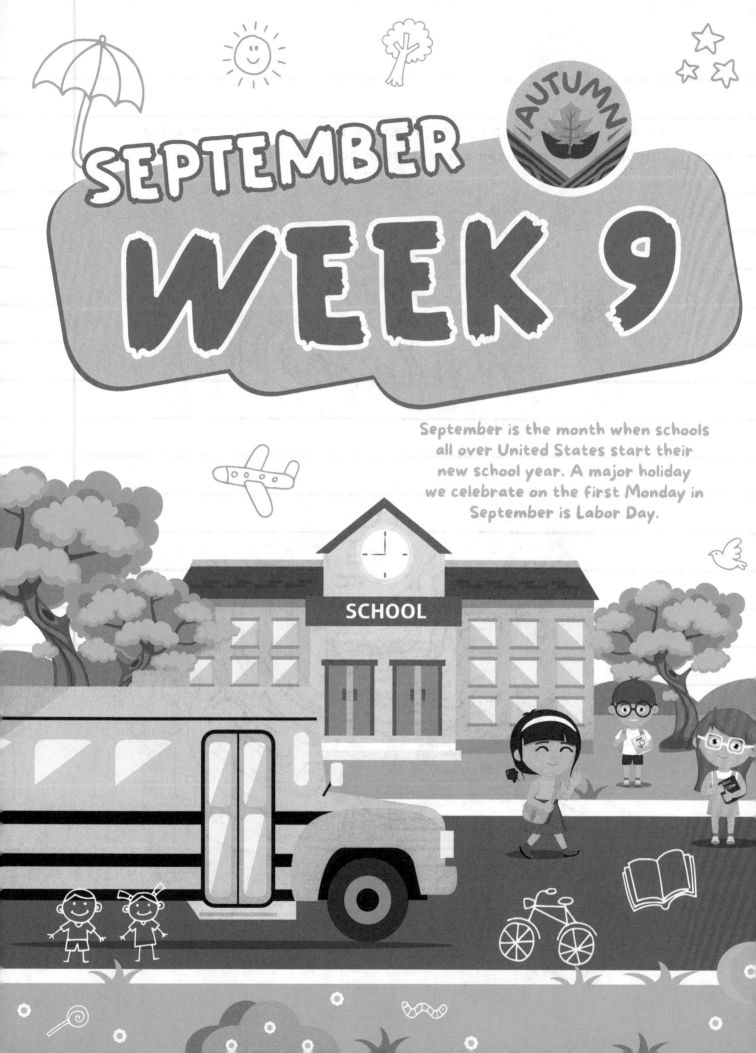

September is the month when schools all over United States start their new school year. A major holiday we celebrate on the first Monday in September is Labor Day.

SCHOOL

AUTUMN

## Responding to a Literary Text

When you first started to read books, the main goal was just for you to correctly understand what was going on. You were trying to understand who the characters were and what events happened in the plot. Now that you've mastered picking up simple concepts like that, it's time to train your brain in a different way: you need to start thinking about **responding to texts**.

When you **respond** to a text, you have the chance to express your own thoughts and connect the text to your own life or experience. In a way, **responding** to a text is like the opposite of the **text-based questions** we looked at last week. A response is all about <u>**your** thoughts and feelings.</u> With that said, to write a strong response, you still need a strong understanding of what you read!

<u>Key Terms</u>

Literary Text: A text (book, TV show, movie, etc.) that tells a <u>story</u>

<u>When You're Asked to Respond to a Text...</u>

- Read the question or writing prompt **extra carefully**

  o Make sure you **understand what you're supposed to be writing about**
  o If you misunderstand this part, your response might be incorrect no matter how much thought you put into it!

- Take a few minutes to <u>plan your response</u>

  o If you just jump in and start writing, you might run out of steam or start **rambling** with your writing!
  o Use some time to **think** about the question
  o You can jot down a few **notes** to help you organize your thoughts before you start writing!

Common Response Types for Literary Texts:

When you read/review a literary text or story, you might be asked to do things like...

- Discuss how the story (or a certain scene) **made you feel**

- Explain **whether you agree or disagree** with the way characters acted

- Think about **how you would approach** certain problems or situations in the story

- Describe whether you **liked or disliked** the story

Writing a Response:

- <u>Start</u> your response by **explaining how you feel as clearly as possible** in one sentence

- <u>Stay focused</u> on the actual question/writing prompt!

- Remember to **refer to specific examples or details from the text** to explain what you're talking about!

## From "Lodrix the Little Lake Dweller"
## By Grace Willard Edick& Belle Wiley

Many years ago, there lived in the high regions of Switzerland and France a people called the Lake-Dwellers.

These people did not live on land, as we do, but on the many lakes hidden among the high mountains.

The mountain-sides were thick with forests which hid the lake-houses from the people who lived on the land. Lodrix was the chief's son, and he was a very brave boy though he was only twelve years old.

This little boy had blonde hair and blue eyes. His fair skin was very much tanned, because he was out of doors much of the time. His clothing was of deerskin and was thrown loosely about him."

Lodrix looked very much like his mother, but her dress was very different.

Her waist was of coarse brown cloth fastened under a skirt of deerskin, and her shoulders and arms were bare.

Her thick light hair was coiled on the top of her head and had many bone and bronze pins in it.

Around her neck were beads of amber, bone and glass, and a necklace made from the teeth of wolves.

On her arms and legs she wore wide bronze bracelets. She was very proud of them, because not many women among the Lake-Dwellers had bracelets made of bronze.

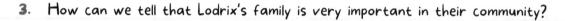

1.  **Underline** at least three details in the passage that help you understand what **Lodrix** looks like.

2.  According to the passage, what is the main **difference** between <u>Lodrix</u> and <u>his mother</u> in terms of the way they **look**?

    **A.** She looks much older than he does
    **B.** He has light hair and she has dark hair
    **C.** She is much taller than him
    **D.** They wear very different clothes

3.  How can we tell that Lodrix's family is very important in their community?

    **A.** Lodrix is the chief
    **B.** Lodrix's mother is the chief
    **C.** Lodrix's father is the chief
    **D.** Lodrix's mother wears a lot of fancy jewelry

4.  What are **three different pieces of jewelry** that Lodrix's mother is described wearing?

    o _____

    o _____

    o _____

5.  **Based on the passage**, would you want to <u>dress</u> like Lodrix and his family? Why or why not?

    _____

    _____

    _____

    _____

    _____

## Responding to a Literary Text

**Directions:** Think about **the passage you just read as part of the reading comprehension activity** and read the writing prompt below. Write a response of 3-5 sentences on the lines below. Remember...

- Make sure you write about the aspect of the text you're supposed to respond to

- Mention specific moments or ideas from the passage that stuck out to you

- Try to explain how **reading** and **thinking** about the text made you feel

**PROMPT:** Lodrix and his Lake-Dweller family live hidden away from the rest of the world near a lake high in the mountains. **How do you think** living far away from most other people like that would **feel**? Do you think you would like living in an isolated setting, like Lodrix and his family? **Why** or why not?

**YOUR RESPONSE:**

_____

_____

_____

_____

_____

_____

_____

_____

_____

_____

_____

_____

_____

_____

_____

_____

_____

_____

_____

## FITNESS

Please be aware of your environment and be safe at all times. If you cannot do an exercise, just try your best.

Repeat these **exercises 3 ROUNDS**

**2 - Lunges: 2** times to each leg.
Note: Use your body weight or books as weight to do leg lunges.

**1 - Abs: 3** times

**4 - Run: 50**m
Note: Run **25** meters to one side and **25** meters back to the starting position.

**3 - Plank: 6** sec.

## From "*Lodrix the Little Lake Dweller*"
## By Grace Willard Edick& Belle Wiley

Lodrix's father, the chief of the Dormorants, was a very brave man.

His people loved him and always obeyed him.

One day, when the chief and his son were on the lake fishing, they heard the sound of a horn.

Lodrix listened, then said, "That is mother's call; she must need us."

In great haste they paddled toward the sound of the horn, and across the lake they could see the mother waving her hands to them.

She stood on a platform which was built upon thousands of wooden piles, driven into the bottom of the lake.

These piles were held in place by stones and rushes that had been let down into the water.

As they paddled nearer, they could see that something had happened.

They hurried to climb the notched ladder which led to the platform.

Then they followed the mother into the one-room hut which was their home.

1. **Underline** the part of the text where it explains how Lodrix and his father knew to come home from their fishing trip.

2. Based on Day I's passage and this passage, why are Lodrix's people called the "Lake-Dwellers?"

   A. They live underwater in a lake
   B. The live near lakes
   C. They live on wooden platforms built on top of a lake
   D. They like lakes

**3.** Why do you think Lodrix and his father were fishing together at the beginning of the story?

_____

_____

**4.** Based on the text, which of these words probably <u>means the same</u> thing as "**piles?**"

   **A.** Sticks
   **B.** Logs
   **C.** Rocks
   **D.** Mountains

**5.** Based on what you've read so far, **make a prediction** about what problem Lodrix's mother might be about to tell Lodrix and his father about. What do you think might be wrong?

_____

_____

_____

_____

_____

## Responding to a Literary Text (Part 2)

**Directions:** Think about **the passage you just read as part of the reading comprehension activity** and read the writing prompt below. Write a response of 3-5 sentences on the lines below. Remember...

- Make sure you write about the aspect of the text you're supposed to respond to

- Mention specific moments or ideas from the passage that stuck out to you

- Try to explain how **reading** and **thinking** about the text <u>made you feel</u>

**PROMPT:** Now that you've read a better depiction of how **Lodrix and his family live,** what do you think would be the **advantages** and **disadvantages** of living on top of a lake? What aspects of what you read seem like they might be cool? Which ones sounded bad, scary, or frustrating?

**YOUR RESPONSE:**

_____

_____

_____

_____

_____

_____

_____

_____

_____

_____

# FITNESS

Please be aware of your environment and be safe at all times. If you cannot do an exercise, just try your best.

Repeat these **exercises 3 ROUNDS**

**2 - Side Bending:** 5 times to each side. Note: try to touch your feet.

**3 - Tree Pose:** Stay as long as possible. Note: do the same with the other leg.

**1 - Squats: 5** times. Note: imagine you are trying to sit on a chair.

## Identifying number patterns

1. The rule for the pattern shown below is "+ 2". Fill in the missing numbers.

    3, ⌢, 7, 9, ⌢, 13

    〰〰〰〰〰〰〰

2. What rule is used for the pattern?

    〰〰〰〰〰〰〰

3. Which rule describes the pattern: 3, 7, 11, 15?

    A. + 2
    B. + 3
    C. + 4
    D. + 5

4. Look at the pattern below.

    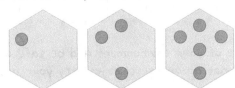

    What "rule" is being used?

    〰〰〰〰〰〰〰

    What might the next shape look like?

5. The number pattern is "times 2". Which number is after 5, 10, 20 ?

    A. 30
    B. 40
    C. 50
    D. 60

6. What rule is used for the pattern?

    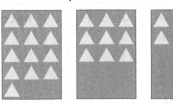

    〰〰〰〰〰〰〰

7. The rule for the pattern shown is "- 3". Fill in the missing numbers.

    32, 29, ⌢, 23, ⌢, 17

    〰〰〰〰〰〰〰

8. Look at the pattern below.

    What "rule" is being used?

    〰〰〰〰〰〰〰

    What might the next shape look like?

9. The rule for the pattern shown below is "add 5". Fill in the missing numbers.

    4, 9, ⌢, 19, ⌢, 29

10. What rule is used for the pattern?

    〰〰〰〰〰〰〰

11. Determine what rule is used for the pattern 42, 36, 30, 24, 18.

    A. Add 5
    B. Add 6
    C. Subtract 5
    D. Subtract 6

**12.** What rule is used for the pattern?

~~~~~~~~~~~~~~~~~~~~~~~~~~~~~

**13.** The number pattern is "times 5". Which number is the next 2, 10, 50, ____?

  A. 200
  B. 250
  C. 300
  D. 350

**14.** What rule is used for the pattern 21, 28, 35, 42?

  A. Add 6
  B. Add 7
  C. Times 2
  D. Times 3

**15.** Look at the pattern below.

What "rule" is being used?

~~~~~~~~~~~~~~~~~~~~~~~~~~~~~

What might the next shape look like?

**16.** In the pattern 3, 6, 9, 12. If the pattern continues what will be the 10th number in the pattern?

  A. 27
  B. 29
  C. 30
  D. 33

**17.** Madison listed these numbers: 88, 81, 74, 67, 60. What rule did Madison use?

~~~~~~~~~~~~~~~~~~~~~~~~~~~~~

# FITNESS

Please be aware of your environment and be safe at all times. If you cannot do an exercise, just try your best.

Repeat these **exercises 3 ROUNDS**

**2 - Lunges:** 3 times to each leg.
Note: Use your body weight or books as weight to do leg lunges.

**3 - Plank:** 6 sec.

**1 - Bend forward:** 10 times.
Note: try to touch your feet. Make sure to keep your back straight and if needed you can bend your knees.

**4 - Abs:** 10 times

## Various Real World Word Problems

1. Farmer Andrew has 72 cucumber plants to plant. If he divides them equally among 8 rows, how many cucumber plants will be in each row?

   A. 6           C. 8
   B. 7           D. 9

2. Chloe has 450 yellow beads and 126 pink beads. How many beads does she have altogether?

3. The shaded portion below represents how much pizza Janice ate. If she eats three more pieces, what fraction of the pizza will be left?

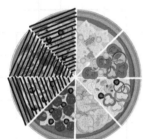

   A. $\dfrac{4}{8}$      C. $\dfrac{2}{8}$

   B. $\dfrac{3}{8}$      D. $\dfrac{1}{8}$

4. Alex had four boxes of balls. Each box has white, brown, pink, violet, and orange balls in it. There were 4 of each type of ball in every box. How many balls did he have in total?

   A. 60          C. 76
   B. 68          D. 80

5. The gym teacher, Mr. O'Connor, has 4 boxes of volleyballs with five volleyballs in each box. He also has 3 boxes of basketballs with seven basketballs in each box. How many more basketballs than volleyballs does he have in the gym?

6. Craig has 7 toy cars in each of the boxes below. How many toy cars does he have in all?

7. David arrived at the railway station at 1:25 pm. If it took him 45 minutes to drive there, what time did he leave for the railway station?

   A. 12:10       C. 12:45
   B. 12:40       D. 12:55

8. The temperature inside a house was 20°C, which was 5°C warmer than the temperature outside. What temperature was it outside?

9. There are three times as many strawberry plants as there are radish plants. If there are 21 radish plants, how many strawberry plants are there?

10. There were **25** chairs in each classroom. If there were **12** classrooms, how many chairs were there in the school?

    **A.** 250          **C.** 300

    **B.** 275          **D.** 325

11. Lily, Natalie, and Daniel sold cookies at a charity fair. Lily earned **$36** and Natalie earned **$25**. Together, Lily and Natalie earned **$18** more than Daniel. How much money did Daniel earn?

12. Michael finished doing his homework at 7:15 p.m. If he had started working it at 5:35 p.m., how long did it take him to do his homework?

    **A.** 1 hour and 40 minutes
    **B.** 2 hours
    **C.** 2 hours and 10 minutes
    **D.** 2 hours and 15 minutes

13. Doris bought **6** plates at a store. If each plate cost **$6** and **10¢** and she paid with a fifty dollar bill, how much change should she get back?

    **A.** $13 and 40¢
    **B.** $13 and 50¢
    **C.** $13 and 60¢
    **D.** $13 and 70¢

14. The bus was scheduled to arrive at 3:35 p.m. However, it was delayed for 25 minutes. What time was it when the bus arrived?

15. A group of 12 girls and 15 boys are planning a camping trip. Each tent can hold 3 kids. How many tents will the group need?

# FITNESS

Repeat these **exercises 3 ROUNDS**

Please be aware of your environment and be safe at all times. If you cannot do an exercise, just try your best.

**1 - High Plank:** 6 sec.

**2 - Chair:** 10 sec. Note: sit on an imaginary chair, keep your back straight.

**4 - Abs:** 10 times

**3 - Waist Hooping:** 10 times. Note: if you do not have a hoop, pretend you have an imaginary hoop and rotate your hips 10 times.

## Various Real World Word Problems

1. Terry and Max have gardens of the same size. Max used **26** ft² of his garden to plant tulips. Terry used **46** ft² of his garden to plant tulips. Who has more garden space left?

   ~~~~~~~~~~~~~~~~~~~~

2. The train departs the railway station every **55** minutes. If the first train is scheduled to depart at **5:55** a.m., when should the third train depart?

   ~~~~~~~~~~~~~~~~~~~~

3. Paula bought a big book that costs **$22**. She also bought **6** smaller books that cost **$4** each. How much do they cost all together?

   **A.** $26    **C.** $46
   **B.** $28    **D.** $48

4. Chris and Mike had an equal number of mushrooms. Chris added $\frac{1}{5}$ more to the amount of his mushrooms. Mike added $\frac{1}{4}$ more the amount of his mushrooms. Who had more mushrooms?

   ~~~~~~~~~~~~~~~~~~~~

5. There are two bridges over a river. The longer bridge is **140** yards. The shorter bridge is **12** yards shorter than half the length of the longer bridge. What is the length of the shorter bridge?

   **A.** 66 yd    **C.** 54 yd
   **B.** 58 yd    **D.** 50 yd

6. A large bag of flour weighed **64** pounds. A small bag of flour weighed **27** pounds. What is the difference in weight between the two bags?

   ~~~~~~~~~~~~~~~~~~~~

## Line of symmetry

1. Does this apple have symmetry?

   Yes                    No

2. Does this picture have symmetry?

   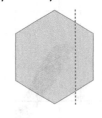

   Yes                    No

3. Which of the shapes below does have symmetry?

   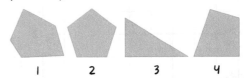

   1        2        3        4

   **A.** 1    **C.** 3
   **B.** 2    **D.** 4

4. Determine if the line through the figure is a line of symmetry.

   ~~~~~~~~~~~~~~~~~~~~

5. How many lines of symmetry does this shape have?

_____

6. Does a ball have symmetry?

Yes                    No

7. Which shape appears to have EXACTLY 1 line of symmetry?

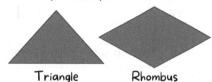

Triangle          Rhombus

_____

8. Which shape appears to have EXACTLY 2 lines of symmetry?

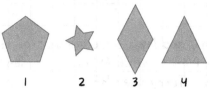

    1        2        3        4

_____

9. Draw a line of symmetry for this shape.

Answer: _____

10. Determine if the line through the figure is a line of symmetry.

_____

 YOGA

Please be aware of your environment and be safe at all times. If you cannot do an exercise, just try your best.

**1 - Down Dog:** 10 sec.

**2 - Bend Down:** 10 sec.

**3 - Chair:** 10 sec.

**4 - Child Pose:** 20 sec.

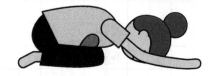

**5 - Shavasana:** as long as you can.
Note: think of happy moments and relax your mind.

## Preventing Erosion

Last week, we built sand mountains and exposed them to water and wind to get a sense of how erosion works. Today, we'll try to think like engineers to see what we can do about preventing erosion and protecting people who live in areas that are at risk of erosion.

### Materials:

- A paint roller tray (available at the hardware store)
- Room temperature running water
- A small watering can or glass
- A freezer bag of soil (can be any outdoor soil)
- A small fan (handheld is ideal)
- A few drops of blue food coloring (optional)
- A few small pieces of sturdy paper or light cardboard.
- Assorted crafting materials (popsicle sticks, clay, etc.)
- Small rocks, sticks, or other small objects gathered from outside

### Procedure:

1. Set your paint roller tray on a flat surface. Using your soil, cover the declining (ramp-like) part of the roller tray with an even layer of soil that you obtained from outside or a garden center.

2. Using sturdy paper or light cardboard, cut out a few shapes that look like **houses** (they don't have to be big – just focus on making about **5** of them). Attach a piece of cardboard to the bottom of your house as a **base**, so it can stand up in the paint tray.

3. Place the houses you created toward the bottom of the slope of the paint tray (near the edge of your dirt and near the reservoir where paint goes). These houses represent places where people live near water.

4. Fill the paint reservoir at the bottom of the tray about $\frac{3}{4}$ full with water (you can add some blue food coloring to make things more dramatic).

5. Using the watering can, simulate some "rain" coming down on the area of dirt and observe what happens as that water runs down toward the bottom of the paint tray.

6. Turn on your handheld fan (<u>gently</u> at first) so that it blows down the ramp of the paint tray, and observe what happens to the soil.

7. Turn off the fan and **brainstorm** some ways you could prevent soil (and potentially houses) from washing down into the reservoir.

8. Using sticks, stones, and whatever crafting tools you have around, try to create a system that will allow water to drain and prevent the houses from falling into the water.

1. After you've built your erosion prevention system, test it by adding some more rain and wind. If your system doesn't work, try adding some new elements. If it does work, try to figure out what made your system effective.

2. Answer the questions below and clean up your materials.

## Follow-Up Questions:

1. Based on what you saw, why is living <u>near the water</u> especially challenging?

_____

_____

_____

2. What was one way you were able to keep the water <u>away from the houses</u>?

_____

_____

# YOGA

Please be aware of your environment and be safe at all times. If you cannot do an exercise, just try your best.

**1 - Tree Pose:**
Stay as long as possible.
Note: do on one leg then on another.

**2 - Down Dog:**
10 sec.

**3 - Stretching:**
Stay as long as possible. Note: do on one leg then on another.

**5 - Book Pose:** 6 sec.
Note: Keep your core tight. Legs should be across from your eyes.

**6 - Shavasana:** 5 min.
Note: this pose is very important and provides you with long term benefits. Try not to skip this. Close your eyes and imagine who you want to be and what your goals are! Always think happy thoughts.

**4 - Lower Plank:** 6 sec.
Note: Keep your back straight and body tight.

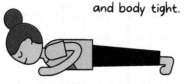

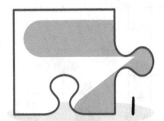
1

2

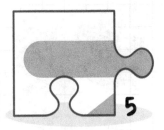
3

4

## ABC

Find the missing
piece of the puzzle.

5

6

7

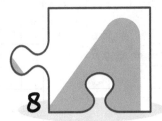
8

193

# OVERVIEW OF ENGLISH CONCEPTS

## Facts, Opinions, and Claims

When you read or watch something, it's <u>incredibly</u> important for you to be able to tell whether what you're reading or hearing is **fact, opinion,** or a **claim**. This sounds straightforward at first, but many people intentionally try to present their opinions <u>as though they're facts,</u> which means you have to get good at recognizing the difference!

This week, we'll explain what each of those three terms means, and you'll have some opportunities to practice thinking about fact, opinion, and claims.

### Key Terms:

Fact: Something that is definitely true.

- Facts can be **double-checked, looked up,** or **confirmed**

- For example...

  o The sky is blue.
  o Water is wet.
  o My first grade teacher's name was Ms. Jan.

Opinion: A person's belief or preference about what is best or true based on their feelings.

- Opinions reflect how a certain person or group of people **feel**

- For example...

  o Red balloons are my favorite.
  o Chocolate cake is the best!
  o Ms. Jan was the greatest teacher I ever had.

Claim: A strongly held belief that can be defended or argued against using facts.

- Claims are <u>based in **feelings and beliefs,**</u> like opinions, but use **facts** as evidence or "backup"
- For example...

  o Global climate change is the biggest threat to humanity.

- This statement is rooted in **belief**, but someone could provide scientific data and facts to explain their thinking to someone else and show them why they think others should feel that way.

o The town should lower taxes.

- This statement is rooted in **belief**, but people who agreed and disagreed could have a **debate** about the idea based on **facts** and **evidence** - that makes it <u>more than an opinion.</u>

<u>Telling an Opinion from a Claim</u>

- **Ask yourself:** Is this <u>just a belief</u>, or is it rooted in an <u>interpretation of facts?</u>

o For example...

o "Vanilla ice cream is the best!" is an **opinion** because someone could easily disagree without being necessarily right or wrong.

o "Ice cream cannot be part of a healthy diet!" is a **claim** because two people who disagreed could debate or argue that point by citing different facts or statistics.

## From "Lodrix the Little Lake Dweller"
## By Grace Willard Edick& Belle Wiley
## (Continued from Week 9's Passages)

Then they followed the mother into the one-room hut which was their home.

They sat down on blocks of wood about the stone fire-place, while the mother told the chief what had happened.

She said that one of their tribe, who had just returned from hunting, had told her that the Bear tribe on the land was getting ready to burn down the Lake-Dweller homes.

When Lodrix heard this, he ran to his father and said, "May I get ready to fight, father?"

The chief put his hands on his son's head, saying, "My brave boy."

Then he told Lodrix to go out and call the people together.

Soon they came, hundreds of them, from the many square huts which were crowded about the chief's home.

...

While Lodrix summoned the people, the chief rushed out to pull back the drawbridge which connected their homes with the land.

The lake people were very much frightened. They knew that the people on land were their enemies; so they were ready to obey every command of their chief.

1. **Underline** the part of the text where it explains how Lodrix's mother heard about the plan to attack their village.

2. According to the passage, how do the **lake people** react to news that they may be attacked?

_____

_____

_____

3. Why does Lodrix's father call him "my brave boy?"

   **A.** Because he discovered the Bear tribe's plan to attack the village

   **B.** Because he is an excellent hunter and fisherman

   **C.** Because he is willing to call the people together

   **D.** Because he volunteered to fight, even though he is young

4. According to the text, what kind of weapon was the Bear tribe going to use to attack Lodrix's village?

   **A.** Arrows

   **B.** A Catapult

   **C.** Fire

   **D.** Swords

5. If you were in Lodrix's father's position as chief, what kind of a plan would you suggest to protect the lake village from outside attackers? Be creative and try to think about how you would defend the lake people.

_____

_____

_____

_____

_____

## Assessing Fact, Claim, and Opinion (Part 1)

**Directions:** Read each statement below and determine if it is a **fact, claim, or opinion**. Write your answer on the line below, then explain what ideas or words from the sentence led you to your choice. (Note: None of the statements below are intentionally lies or misleading.)

1. Big Wheels Cola is my favorite soft drink.

**Fact, Claim or Opinion** _____

**How do you know?** _____

_____

_____

2. In 2018, based on how much money it earned, *Incredibles* **2** was one of the most successful movies of the year.

**Fact, Claim or Opinion** _____

**How do you know?** _____

_____

_____

3. If everybody drove electric cars, the United States would be a better country.

**Fact, Claim or Opinion** _____

**How do you know?** _____

_____

_____

199

4.  World War II took place between 1939 and 1945.

**Fact, Claim** or **Opinion** _____

**How do you know?** _____

_____

_____

_____

_____

_____

_____

# FITNESS

Please be aware of your environment and be safe at all times. If you cannot do an exercise, just try your best.

Repeat these **exercises 3 ROUNDS**

**2 - Lunges:** 2 times to each leg.
Note: Use your body weight or books as weight to do leg lunges.

**1 - Abs:** 3 times

**3 - Plank:** 6 sec.

**4 - Run:** 50m
Note: Run 25 meters to one side and 25 meters back to the starting position.

### From "Lodrix the Little Lake Dweller"
### By Grace Willard Edick& Belle Wiley
### (Continued from Day 1's Passage)

First Lodrix's father called for the messenger who had brought the news.

A youth with a deer hanging from his shoulder stepped forward.

Laying the deer at the chief's feet, the boy said, "My chief! As I was hunting, I met the boy Tevico, whom you once saved from the wolves in the forest.
"He told me that his tribe was getting ready to make war upon us and to burn our dwellings.

"So I hurried here to tell you, that we, too, might prepare for war."

Just then Lodrix, running into the house, shouted, "O father! Come quickly!"

Out rushed the chief, followed by his people.

What they saw made them tremble with fear.

On the shore of the lake stood hundreds of people waving their stone axes and shouting in great anger.
The chief had pulled up the drawbridge just in time.

When the Bear people found they could not reach the Lake-Dwellers, they went away.

The chief of the Dormorants told his people that they must keep close watch, for their enemies would surely come back.

1. **Underline** the place in the text that shows what animal the young messenger was hunting when he learned about the attack.

2. How does Tevico (of the Bear tribe) know Lodrix's father?

_____

_____

_____

_____

3. Which weapon does this passage specifically mention the Bear tribe using?

   **A.** Swords
   **B.** Arrows
   **C.** Axes
   **D.** Fire

4. How does Lodrix's father prevent the Bear tribe from reaching their village?

   **A.** Magic
   **B.** He raises the drawbridges
   **C.** He burns their boats with flaming arrows
   **D.** He scares them off by yeling at them

5. If you were Lodrix's father (the chief), **what would you do next**? Would you try to increase the village's defenses, gather a group of warriors to go fight the Bear tribe on land, or do something else completely different? Explain your plan for saving the day in a few sentences below:

_____

_____

_____

_____

_____

## Assessing Fact, Claim, and Opinion (Part 2)

**Directions:** Read each statement below and determine if it is a **fact, claim, or opinion**. Write your answer on the line below, then explain what ideas or words from the sentence led you to your choice. (Note: None of the statements below are intentionally lies or misleading.)

1.  Uncle Ross is the funniest person in my family.

**Fact, Claim** or **Opinion** _____

**How do you know?** _____

_____

2.  McGillicutty paint brushes are the best brushes money can buy.

**Fact, Claim** or **Opinion** _____

**How do you know?** _____

_____

3.  Aunt Portia is about five feet tall.

**Fact, Claim** or **Opinion** _____

**How do you know?** _____

_____

4. Canned whipped cream is the best!

**Fact, Claim** or **Opinion** _____

**How do you know?** _____

_____

_____

_____

## FITNES

Repeat these **excersises** **3 ROUNDS**

Please be aware of your environment and be safe at all times. If you cannot do an exercise, just try your best.

**2 - Side Bending:** 5 times to each side. Note: try to touch your feet.

**3 - Tree Pose:** Stay as long as possible. Note: do the same with the other leg.

**1 - Squats:** 5 times. Note: imagine you are trying to sit on a chair.

### Number Lines

1. Determine which letter best shows the location of the fraction $\frac{3}{4}$.

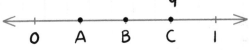

---

2. What fractions do the letters in the number line represent?

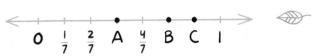

---

3. Put the dot at $\frac{3}{5}$ on the number line.

4. Which point is at $\frac{4}{5}$ on the number line?

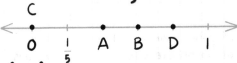

   **A.** A
   **B.** B
   **C.** C
   **D.** D

5. What fraction does the number line show?

   **A.** $\frac{1}{6}$          **C.** $\frac{3}{6}$

   **B.** $\frac{2}{6}$          **D.** $\frac{4}{6}$

6. Graph $\frac{7}{8}$ on the number line.

7. Which number line shows a marked segment with a length of $\frac{3}{4}$?

   A.

   B.

   C.

8. Which fraction does the marked segment represent?

   **A.** $\frac{1}{6}$          **C.** $\frac{3}{6}$

   **B.** $\frac{2}{6}$          **D.** $\frac{4}{6}$

9. Which point is at $\frac{4}{5}$ on the number line?

   **A.** A          **C.** C
   **B.** B          **D.** D

10. Determine which letter best shows the location of the fraction $\frac{4}{7}$.

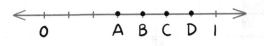

   **A.** A          **C.** C
   **B.** B          **D.** D

205

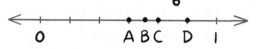

11. Which point is at $\frac{7}{9}$ on the number line?

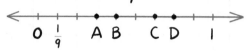

   A. A
   B. B
   C. C
   D. D

12. Graph $\frac{5}{8}$ on the number line.

13. What fraction is located at Point C on the number line?

14. Determine which letter best shows the location of the fraction $\frac{3}{6}$.

   A. A
   B. B
   C. C
   D. D

15. Which number line shows a marked segment with a length of $\frac{4}{6}$?

   A.

   B.

   C.

# FITNESS

Repeat these exercises **3 ROUNDS**

Please be aware of your environment and be safe at all times. If you cannot do an exercise, just try your best.

**1 - Bend forward:** 10 times.
Note: try to touch your feet. Make sure to keep your back straight and if needed you can bend your knees.

**2 - Lunges:** 3 times to each leg.
Note: Use your body weight or books as weight to do leg lunges.

3 - Plank: 6 sec.

**4 - Abs:** 10 times

Express whole numbers as fractions and recognize fractions that are equivalent to whole numbers.

1. Write $\frac{17}{17}$ as a whole number.

   ～～～～～～～～～～～～

2. Which point is at 1 on the number line?

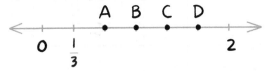

   A. A
   B. B
   C. C
   D. D

3. Which point is at 3 on the number line?

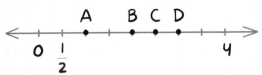

   A. A
   B. B
   C. C
   D. D

4. Which picture shows $\frac{6}{6}$ = 1?

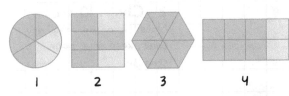

   1      2       3        4

   ～～～～～～～～～～～～

5. Which fraction is equivalent to 1?

   A. $\frac{5}{6}$         C. $\frac{4}{2}$

   B. $\frac{7}{7}$         D. $\frac{9}{8}$

6. Write 8 as a fraction with 1 in the denominator.

   ～～～～～～～～～～～～

7. Graph $\frac{4}{4}$ on the number line.

   Answer: ～～～～～～～～～～

8. Count the parts in the whole. Then choose the fraction for the whole.

   A. $\frac{8}{9}$         C. $\frac{9}{8}$

   B. $\frac{7}{8}$         D. $\frac{9}{9}$

9. Which point is at 1 on the number line?

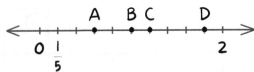

   A. A
   B. B
   C. C
   D. D

207

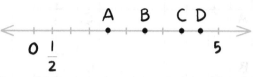

**10.** Which point is at 4 on the number line?

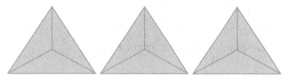

A B C D

0 $\frac{1}{2}$          5

**A.** A          **C.** C
**B.** B          **D.** D

**11.** Represent the diagram below as a fraction with **3** being the denominator.

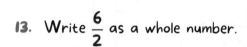

~~~~~~~~~~~~~~~~~~~~~~

**12.** Write the missing number to complete the equivalent fraction.

$$1 = \frac{3}{3} = \frac{?}{9}$$

**13.** Write $\frac{6}{2}$ as a whole number.

~~~~~~~~~~~~~~~~~~~~~~

**14.** Write **20** as a fraction with **1** in the denominator.

~~~~~~~~~~~~~~~~~~~~~~

**15.** Which fraction is equivalent to 2?

**A.** $\frac{1}{2}$          **C.** $\frac{2}{1}$

**B.** $\frac{5}{5}$          **D.** $\frac{5}{2}$

**16.** Graph 1 on the number line.

0 $\frac{1}{6}$

# FITNESS

Please be aware of your environment and be safe at all times. If you cannot do an exercise, just try your best.

Repeat these **exercises 3 ROUNDS**

**2 - Chair:** 10 sec.
Note: sit on an imaginary chair, keep your back straight.

**1 - High Plank:** 6 sec.

**4 - Abs:** 10 times

**3 - Waist Hooping:** 10 times. Note: if you do not have a hoop, pretend you have an imaginary hoop and rotate your hips 10 times.

Compare two fractions with the same numerator or the same denominator by reasoning about their size.

1. Use < or > to compare the fractions below.

$$\frac{3}{8} \text{ and } \frac{5}{8}$$

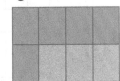

2. Which fraction can be used to make the number sentence true?

$$\underline{\hspace{2cm}} > \frac{4}{6}$$

A. $\frac{5}{6}$     C. $\frac{2}{6}$

B. $\frac{3}{6}$     D. $\frac{1}{6}$

3. Compare $\frac{1}{3}$ and $\frac{2}{3}$.

$$\frac{1}{3}$$

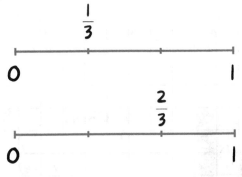

0                    1

$$\frac{2}{3}$$

0                    1

4. Compare $\frac{2}{5}$ and $\frac{2}{6}$.

5. Which number sentence below is true?

A. $\frac{1}{2} = \frac{1}{4}$     C. $\frac{2}{3} > \frac{2}{4}$

B. $\frac{3}{5} < \frac{3}{6}$     D. $\frac{6}{7} < \frac{5}{7}$

6. Which expression could represent the models below?

A. $\frac{4}{8} = \frac{5}{8}$     C. $\frac{4}{8} < \frac{5}{8}$

B. $\frac{4}{8} > \frac{5}{8}$     D. $\frac{5}{8} < \frac{4}{8}$

7. Determine which fraction shown below is 'less' than $\frac{4}{9}$.

A. $\frac{4}{6}$     C. $\frac{4}{7}$

B. $\frac{4}{5}$     D. $\frac{4}{10}$

8. Sophie ate $\frac{1}{3}$ of the pizza and Rebecca ate $\frac{1}{2}$ of the same pizza. Which statement is true?

A. $\frac{1}{3} > \frac{1}{2}$     C. $\frac{1}{3} = \frac{1}{2}$

B. $\frac{1}{3} < \frac{1}{2}$     D. $\frac{1}{3} > \frac{1}{2}$

9. Use '>', '<', or '=' to compare the fractions $\frac{5}{8}$ and $\frac{3}{8}$.

~~~~~~~~~~~~~~~~~~~~~~~~~~~~~

10. Order the following fractions from greatest to smallest $\frac{3}{8}, \frac{3}{4}, \frac{3}{6}, \frac{3}{5}$.

~~~~~~~~~~~~~~~~~~~~~~~~~~~~~

11. Determine if $\frac{8}{12}$ is 'less', 'more', or 'equal to' $\frac{6}{12}$.

~~~~~~~~~~~~~~~~~~~~~~~~~~~~~

12. Which fraction is equal to the shaded part in the model below?

A. $\frac{4}{7}$    C. $\frac{5}{8}$

B. $\frac{5}{7}$    D. $\frac{6}{8}$

13. Compare $\frac{6}{12}$ and $\frac{6}{15}$, using '>', '<', or '='.

~~~~~~~~~~~~~~~~~~~~~~~~~~~~~

14. Determine which shaded amount is 'greater' than $\frac{3}{5}$.

~~~~~~~~~~~~~~~~~~~~~~~~~~~~~

# YOGA

Please be aware of your environment and be safe at all times. If you cannot do an exercise, just try your best.

**1 - Down Dog:** 10 sec.

**2 - Bend Down:** 10 sec.

**3 - Chair:** 10 sec.

**4 - Child Pose:** 20 sec.

**5 - Shavasana:** as long as you can. Note: think of happy moments and relax your mind.

## Simulating an Earthquake

We've already talked about **erosion** as an example of a natural force that can be very destructive. **Earthquakes** are another naturally occurring phenomenon that can be extremely dangerous for people, buildings, and animals. When an earthquake occurs, the ground shakes violently, and huge crevices or fissures can open up.

This week, we'll build a model that will help us simulate earthquake-like conditions so we can study them. Then, next week, we'll work on designing an earthquake-resistent structure.

### Materials:

- 2 pieces of strong cardboard, about the size of a piece of paper each
- 2 strong rubber bands
- 2 tennis balls
- Masking tape
- A ruler
- An adult
- A few action figures or other small toys (for testing)

### Procedure:

1. Make sure your two pieces of cardboard are the same size. If they're not <u>ask for an adult's help</u> cutting them evenly.

2. Stack the two pieces of cardboard on top of each other and slide the big rubber bands over the stack you've just created, so the rubber bands look like they divide the cardboard into thirds.

3. Separate the two pieces of cardboard on one side and slide a tennis ball between them, so it's trapped in between the two layers of cardboard.

4. Repeat Step 3, placing the second tennis ball between the two pieces of cardboard on the other side. You should now have something that looks a little like a sandwich, with two tennis balls between two pieces of cardboard and everything held tightly together by two rubber bands.

5. Using some tape, attach the ruler to the bottom of the top piece of cardboard. This will create a handle that you can grab.

6. Grab the handle you just attached and pull it back and forth. The top piece of cardboard should slide around on top of the balls, simulating an earthquake. This is your shaker table!

7. Take a few action figures, dolls, or other small toys and see what happens when you put them on the shaker table and pull the handle. Study which objects fall easily and which ones seem to be sturdier.

8. Answer the questions below and clean up your materials. Save your shaker table because we will be using it next week.

**Follow-Up Questions:**

1. What did you **observe** (see) when you used your shaker table with your toys?

_____

_____

_____

2. How did the **tennis balls** help create the illusion of an <u>earthquake</u>?

_____

_____

_____

Please be aware of your environment and be safe at all times. If you cannot do an exercise, just try your best.

**1 - Tree Pose:**
Stay as long as possible.
Note: do on one leg then on another.

**2 - Down Dog:**
10 sec.

**3 - Stretching:**
Stay as long as possible. Note: do on one leg then on another.

**5 -Book Pose:** 6 sec.
Note: Keep your core tight. Legs should be across from your eyes.

**6 - Shavasana: 5** min.
Note: this pose is very important and provides you with long term benefits. Try not to skip this. Close your eyes and imagine who you want to be and what your goals are! Always think happy thoughts.

**4 - Lower Plank:** 6 sec.
Note: Keep your back straight and body tight.

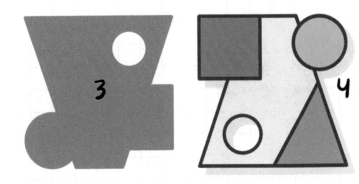

Match the pictures to their shadows.

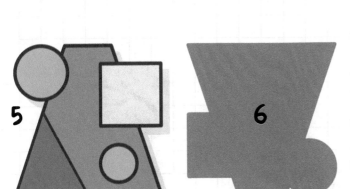

# NOVEMBER
## WEEK 11

AUTUMN

November is the last month of Fall. It is the 11th month of the year and includes 30 days. We celebrate Thanksgiving on the fourth Thursday of November.

## Responding to an Informational Text

A few weeks ago, we introduced the idea of **responding** to a text using your own thoughts, feelings, opinions, and words. We started by **responding** to literary texts (stories), which generally involves discussing how you think or feel about characters or events. This week, we'll look at responding to **informational texts**.

**Informational texts** are designed to help us learn, gain skills, and grow in our understanding of the world. Unlike a story, an informational text probably won't have characters or a "plot" – it will contain concepts and explanations. That means that **responding** requires that you read closely to understand the text before applying your own thinking.

### Key Terms

Informational Text: A text (book, TV show, movie, etc.) that's designed to <u>describe, explain, or teach about</u> a topic.

### When You're Asked to Respond to a Text...

- Read the question or writing prompt **extra carefully**
  - Make sure you **understand what you're supposed to be writing about**
  - If you misunderstand this part, your response might be incorrect no matter how much thought you put into it!
- Take a few minutes to <u>plan your response</u>
  - If you just jump in and start writing, you might run out of steam or start **rambling** with your writing!
  - Use some time to **think** about the question
  - You can jot down a few **notes** to help you organize your thoughts before you start writing!

Common Response Types for Informational Texts:

When you read/review an informational text, you might be asked to do things like...

- Connect the main ideas from the text to **your life**

- Share what information you read was **new or interesting to you**

- Brainstorm situations where the information you read **would be useful**

- **Connect the text to another informational text** you've read or seen (or even a literary text!)

Writing a Response:

- <u>Start</u> your response by **explaining how you feel as clearly as possible** in one sentence
- <u>Stay focused</u> on the actual question/writing prompt!

- Remember to **refer to specific examples or details from the text** to explain what you're talking about!

## From "Devil's Tower National Monument, Wyoming"
## By the National Park Service

Though small in area, Devils Tower National Monument provides a sanctuary for an extensive variety of birds. Because the mountains and the plains converge here, species common to both can be found. More than **90** species have been counted.

Several large birds may be seen flying around or near the Tower itself, occasionally swooping down to prey upon life in the open grasslands. These include Cooper's and red-tailed hawks; American kestrel; golden and bald eagles; prairie falcon, and turkey vulture. Only the prairie falcon and the rock dove, or pigeon, live on the Tower.

The rattle of a kingfisher precedes its sudden appearance around the sharp bend in the river. Skimming low across the water, the blue and white bird darts upward to perch on a cottonwood snag that overhangs the river. Its large crest and straight bill make the kingfisher look more cartoon than real. Intently studying the river below, it need not wait long before diving from its observation post straight into the water. Reappearing a second later, it quickly regains its perch, the silver glint of a small fish caught in the parted scissors of its black bill. After swallowing the fish with a toss of its head, it shakes the water from its feathers and resumes its patient inspection.

1. What is the full name of "the Tower" mentioned in the first sentence of Paragraph 2?

_____

2. **Circle** the names of all the different **birds** mentioned in the passage.

3. According to the text, which of these birds have been seen living on top of the Devil's Tower National Monument?

   A. Turkey Vulture

   B. Prairie Falcon

   C. Bald Eagle

   D. Red-tailed Hawk

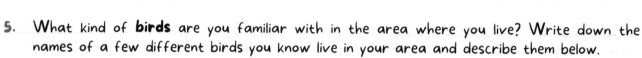

4.  Which of these things is being described in Paragraph 3?

    **A.** A bird catching a fish
    **B.** A fish catching a bird
    **C.** A fisherman catching a fish
    **D.** Two fish fighting

5.  What kind of **birds** are you familiar with in the area where you live? Write down the names of a few different birds you know live in your area and describe them below.

_____

_____

_____

_____

_____

_____

## Responding to an Informational Text (Part 1)

**Directions:** Think about **the passage you just read as part of the reading comprehension activity** and read the writing prompt below. Write a response of 3-5 sentences on the lines below. Remember...

- Make sure you write about the aspect of the text you're supposed to respond to

- Mention specific moments or ideas from the passage that stuck out to you

- Try to explain how **reading** and **thinking** about the text <u>made you feel</u>

**PROMPT:** Does it make you feel sad to think about animals eating each other, as happens in Paragraph 3 of the Day 1 passage? Why or why not? Be sure to give examples from Paragraph 3 to back up what you're saying.

**YOUR RESPONSE:**

_____

_____

_____

_____

_____

_____

_____

_____

_____

_____

_____

---

---

---

---

---

---

---

---

---

# FITNESS

Please be aware of your environment and be safe at all times. If you cannot do an exercise, just try your best.

Repeat these **exercises 3 ROUNDS**

**2 - Lunges:** 2 times to each leg.
Note: Use your body weight or books as weight to do leg lunges.

**1 - Abs:** 3 times

**4 - Run:** 50m
Note: Run **25** meters to one side and **25** meters back to the starting position.

**3 - Plank:** 6 sec.

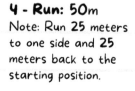

## From "Devil's Tower National Monument, Wyoming"
## By the National Park Service

In the early days of the cattle range, before good land management of the plains was understood, cattlemen were perplexed to witness mushrooming populations of prairie dogs. Formerly lush grassland often became a dog town "wasteland" following the introduction of cattle. Believing that the prairie dog, and not the cattle, was responsible for this sudden transformation, ranchers rapidly came to despise prairie dogs. A massive war of extermination began against these "varmits" that "ate the grass down to nothing."

In reality, the appearance of prairie dogs merely indicated that the land was being overgrazed. As the bison had done before them, cattle now began to open up to the prairie dogs new territories that they could not otherwise colonize. Prairie dogs were never found on the eastern prairies simply because they could not contend with the taller growth of the more humid grasslands.

On their own, prairie dogs cannot easily invade unbroken areas of established grassland. The grass cover simply rejuvenates faster than the animals can work. But if the land has been disturbed by overgrazing, prairie dogs can quickly spread. Once established in an area, the animals wage a constant struggle against the vegetation. Since tall-growing plants offer concealment to a predator, the plants are routinely clipped off even if they are not to be eaten.

1. **Underline** the part of the text that explains why early ranchers on the American prairies disliked prairie dogs.

2. **Circle** the part of the text that explains the connection between cattle and prairie dogs.

3. Based on the passage, which of these is the best definition for "varmit?"

   A. A wild animal that attacks cattle
   B. A particular kind of cattle
   C. A pesky animal that you don't want around
   D. An early cattle rancher

221

4. Which of these environments is the best habitat for prairie dogs?

   **A.** Tall grass

   **B.** Jungle

   **C.** Mountains

   **D.** Short grass

5. What's **one animal** you can think of that can be annoying in the way the cattlemen thought the prairie dogs were? Can you think of any animals that mess with people's property, yards, or garbage? Write down an animal that some people might consider a "nuisance," and describe what it does that angers people:

_____

_____

_____

_____

_____

## Responding to an Informational Text (Part 2)

**Directions:** Think about **the passage you just read as part of the reading comprehension activity** and read the writing prompt below. Write a response of 3-5 sentences on the lines below. Remember...

1. Make sure you write about the aspect of the text you're supposed to respond to

2. Mention specific moments or ideas from the passage that stuck out to you

3. Try to explain how **reading** and **thinking** about the text <u>made you feel</u>

**PROMPT:** Do you think people (like the ranchers and cattlemen in the Day 2 passage) should be able to kill annoying animals near their homes? Why or why not? Be sure to explain what you think and connect your thoughts and feelings to at least one example from the passage.

**YOUR RESPONSE:**

_____

_____

_____

_____

_____

_____

_____

_____

_____

_____

_____

_____

_____

_____

_____

_____

_____

_____

_____

_____

_____

**FITNESS**

Please be aware of your environment and be safe at all times. If you cannot do an exercise, just try your best.

Repeat these **exercises 3 ROUNDS**

**2 - Side Bending:** 5 times to each side. Note: try to touch your feet.

**3 - Tree Pose:** Stay as long as possible. Note: do the same with the other leg.

**1 - Squats: 5** times.
Note: imagine you are trying to sit on a chair.

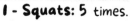

1. What is 27 added to 56?

   A. 83
   B. 86
   C. 88
   D. 93

2. What is the missing number in the following equation?

   $$45 + \underline{\hspace{2cm}} = 60$$

3. What is 16 subtracted from 48?

4. What is the difference between 68 and 34?

   A. 38
   B. 36
   C. 34
   D. 30

5. Find the product of 12 and 3.

   A. 15
   B. 24
   C. 36
   D. 40

6. Which expression describes the model?

   A. 9 x 3
   B. 9 + 3
   C. 3 + 9
   D. 3 x 8

7. What is the quotient when 40 is divided by 10? _____

8. Which equation can be solved by knowing that 9 x 8 = 72?

   A. 9 ÷ 72 =
   B. 8 ÷ 72 =
   C. 72 ÷ 8 =
   D. 72 x 8 =

9. Greg added 8 x 3 to 2 x 4. What was the sum that he got?

   A. 24
   B. 28
   C. 30
   D. 32

10. Zach spent twenty-two minutes playing at school and thirty-two minutes playing at home. How many minutes total did he spend playing?

11. Complete the multiplication sentence that describes the model below.

$$7 \times \underline{\hspace{2cm}} = 42$$

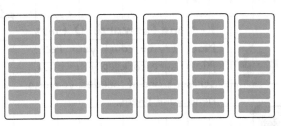

**12.** Write a subtraction sentence based on the picture. ～～～～

～～～～～～～～～～

**13.** Which digit is in the tens place?

421_____

**14.** What is the value of the underlined digit?

56<u>3</u>

A. 3
B. 30
C. 300
D. 3,000

**15.** What is the value of the underlined digit?

<u>5</u>31

A. 5
B. 50
C. 500
D. 5,000

**16.** Write the missing number.

7 hundreds + ～～～～ tens + 1 ones = 751.

A. 1
B. 5
C. 6
D. 7

**17.** Determine the numbers shown in the boxes.

| Hundreds | Tens | Ones |
|----------|------|------|
| ●●● ●●● | ●●● ●● | ●●● |

～～～～～～～～～～～～～～

# FITNESS

Please be aware of your environment and be safe at all times. If you cannot do an exercise, just try your best.

Repeat these
exercises
**3 ROUNDS**

**1 - Bend forward:** 10 times.
Note: try to touch your feet. Make sure to keep your back straight and if needed you can bend your knees.

**2 - Lunges:** 3 times to each leg.
Note: Use your body weight or books as weight to do leg lunges.

**3 - Plank:** 6 sec.

**4 - Abs:** 10 times

1. Write **245** in words.

_____

2. What is **58** rounded to the nearest ten?

_____

3. Which place value do you need to round in the number **266** to get **270**?

   A. Round to the nearest ones place
   B. Round to the nearest tens place
   C. Round to the nearest hundreds place
   D. Round to the nearest thousands place

4. Round **432** to the nearest hundred.

_____

5. Mary had **102** dollars saved up. After doing some chores her mother gave her another **32** dollars. How much money does she have in total?

   A. $70
   B. $124
   C. $134
   D. $136

6. Jamie collected **212** baseball cards. He gave **31** of them to his friend. How many baseball cards does he have now?

   A. 171 baseball cards
   B. 181 baseball cards
   C. 242 baseball cards
   D. 243 baseball cards

7. Leo took **32** marbles from his box. Now he has **18** marbles in his box. How many marbles were originally in there?

_____

8. A restaurant had pepperoni pizza, pizza with mushrooms, and pizza with bacon. If the restaurant had **532** pizzas total, **143** pepperoni pizzas, and **201** pizzas with mushrooms, how many pizzas with bacon did they have?

_____

9. Solve for the following:

   A. 12 - 7 _____
   B. 10 - 0 _____
   C. 11 - 9 _____
   D. 12 - 5 _____

10. Which sum is the least?

    A. 3 + 12
    B. 8 + 6
    C. 4 + 13
    D. 4 + 14

11. What is the missing number in the following equation?

    $$6 + \underline{\qquad} = 17$$

_____

12. Subtract sixteen from nineteen.

_____

**13.** Circle the odd numbers.

5, 2, 1, 3, 6, 4, 9

_____

**14.** Which even number comes next?

34, 36, 38, _____

**15.** Is the number of leaves even or odd?

**A.** Even          **B.** Odd

**16.** Which symbol makes the statement true?

35 ? 37

**A.** >
**B.** <
**C.** =

**17.** Which number is greater, **52** or **39**? Show your answer, using a comparison symbol.

_____

**18.** Which expression is true?

**A.** 71 < 63
**B.** 72 > 81
**C.** 112 > 114
**D.** 49 < 51

**19.** Which expression is FALSE?

**A.** 47 > 35
**B.** 111 = 111
**C.** 32 > 93
**D.** 528 < 532

**20.** Solve for the following:

**A.** 62 + 100 = _____
**B.** 71 + 100 = _____
**C.** 11 + 10 = _____
**D.** 214 + 10 = _____

**FITNESS**

Please be aware of your environment and be safe at all times. If you cannot do an exercise, just try your best.

Repeat these **exercises 3 ROUNDS**

**1 - High Plank:** 6 sec.

**2 - Chair:** 10 sec.
Note: sit on an imaginary chair, keep your back straight.

**4 - Abs:** 10 times

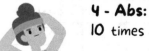

**3 - Waist Hooping:** 10 times. Note: if you do not have a hoop, pretend you have an imaginary hoop and rotate your hips 10 times.

1. Solve for the following:

   **A.** 42 + 100 = ~~~~~
   **B.** 12 + 100 = ~~~~~
   **C.** 109 + 10 = ~~~~~
   **D.** 4 + 10 = ~~~~~

2. Jim has 100 basketball cards, and Frank gifted Jim 10 of his basketball cards. How many basketball cards does Jim have now?

   ~~~~~~~~~~

3. Which expression describes the model?

   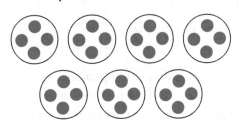

   **A.** 4 + 7
   **B.** 4 × 7
   **C.** 4 + 4 + 4 + 4
   **D.** 7 + 7 + 7 + 7 + 7

4. What is the product of 9 and 8?

   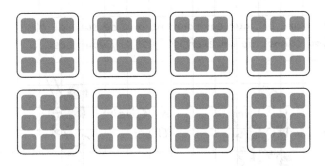

   **A.** 17
   **B.** 45
   **C.** 72
   **D.** 74

5. Find the length of the rectangle using the ruler provided below.

   ~~~~~~~~~~

6. Which is a better estimate for the length of a computer screen?

   **A.** 20 inches
   **B.** 20 feet
   **C.** 20 yards
   **D.** 20 meters

7. The height of a book is about 12 ~~~~~. Choose 'inches', 'feet', 'centimeters', or 'meters' to fill in the blank.

   ~~~~~~~~~~

8. Measure the length of the rectangle in inches and in centimeters.

   **A.** 10 in or 4 cm
   **B.** 2 in or 5 cm
   **C.** 3 in or 5 cm
   **D.** 2 in or 4 cm

9. Which addition sentence does NOT equal 1,000?

   **A.** 555 + 445
   **B.** 612 + 388
   **C.** 289 + 711
   **D.** 212 + 615

10. Which expression represents 3 x 4?

    A. 3 + 4 + 4 + 4
    B. 4 + 4 + 4 + 4
    C. 3 + 3
    D. 3 + 3 + 3 + 3

11. Sheila has only dimes in her pocket. If she has 90 cents in her pocket, how many dimes does she have?

    A. 9 dimes
    B. 10 dimes
    C. 90 dimes
    D. 99 dimes

12. Which number is missing from the equation below?

    $$4 \times (5 \times 9) = (4 \times \underline{\hspace{1cm}}) \times 9$$

    A. 4          C. 9
    B. 5          D. 20

13. Katie has 98 bunches of flowers to sell. She sold 45 bunches this morning, and 23 this afternoon. How many flowers does she have left to sell?

    A. 68 bunches
    B. 53 bunches
    C. 75 bunches
    D. 30 bunches

14. Which of these patterns does NOT follow the rule "add 6"?

    A. 3, 9, 15, 22
    B. 2, 8, 14, 20
    C. 5, 11, 17, 23
    D. 6, 12, 18, 24

15. There are only 35 cupcakes for the party. 5 cupcakes will be put on each table. How many tables can cupcakes be put on?

    A. 4 tables          C. 6 tables
    B. 5 tables          D. 7 tables

YOGA

Please be aware of your environment and be safe at all times. If you cannot do an exercise, just try your best.

**1 - Down Dog:** 10 sec.

**2 - Bend Down:** 10 sec.

**3 - Chair:** 10 sec.

**4 - Child Pose:** 20 sec.

**5 - Shavasana:** as long as you can. Note: think of happy moments and relax your mind.

## Designing an Earthquake-Safe Building

Last week, you created a shaker table to simulate **earthquake** conditions. When you used your table, you probably found that it was difficult for most toys and objects to stay stable on top of it. In areas where earthquakes are common, like the Pacific Rim, designers, engineers, and building architects must create buildings that are built to withstand earthquakes.

Today, you'll be putting on your thinking cap and planning in the same way as you attempt to create an earthquake-resistant building.

### Materials:

- Your shaker table from Week 10's experiment
- Drinking straws or wooden skewers
- Modeling clay
- A few pieces of paper

### Procedure:

1. Set up or reassemble your shaker table from last week as needed.

2. Using your straws/skewers and modeling clay, build a small house. It doesn't need to be fancy or big, but it should have a base and a roof.

3. Once your house is complete, put it on one of your pieces of paper and place it on the shaker table. Pull the handle back and forth to simulate an earthquake for about 10 seconds.

4. After your earthquake is over, observe your house and see how it held up under the conditions. Was it strong and sturdy, or did it come apart? You can write down some notes about performance on your paper, as needed.

5. After observing the performance of your first house, use your clay and straws/skewers to create another house. Try to learn from what you saw the first time. If your house held up well, try building a bigger house. If your house came apart in the earthquake, try building a sturdier house.

6. Repeat steps 3, 4, and 5 until you come up with a design that you're happy with. A strong design will (mostly) survive the earthquake.

7. Answer the questions below and clean up your materials.

**Follow-Up Questions:**

1. What problems did you have with the **first** design you created? What improvements were necessary?

_____

_____

_____

2. What strategies did you find were most helpful for designing something that could withstand an earthquake?

_____

_____

_____

# YOGA

Please be aware of your environment and be safe at all times. If you cannot do an exercise, just try your best.

**1 - Tree Pose:**
Stay as long as possible.
Note: do on one leg then on another.

**2 - Down Dog:**
10 sec.

**3 - Stretching:**
Stay as long as possible. Note: do on one leg then on another.

**5 -Book Pose:** 6 sec.
Note: Keep your core tight. Legs should be across from your eyes.

**6 - Shavasana: 5** min.
Note: this pose is very important and provides you with long term benefits. Try not to skip this. Close your eyes and imagine who you want to be and what your goals are! Always think happy thoughts.

**4 - Lower Plank: 6** sec.
Note: Keep your back straight and body tight.

**Task:** Rhia the rabbit is hungry!

Color in the pathway in the maze so she can eat the carrot.

# DECEMBER
# WEEK 12

**WINTER**

Winter is here! Millions of people all over the world celebrate Christmas and Hanukkah in the month of December.

## Crafting a Narrative

Throughout the summer, you've **read a variety of different texts**, answered **text-based questions,** and generated a variety of **personal responses.** In that time, you've read so many stories written by other people that you've probably gotten some really good ideas for a story of your own. For our final week, we're going to have some fun and talk about a different kind of written response: crafting your own narrative!

This week, you'll be planning and writing a short story that will show off the different reading, thinking, and writing skills that you've developed. Before you do the Day 1 and Day 2 activities this week, be sure to review the "Elements of a Narrative" and "Crafting a Narrative" sections below to get some tips that will help you organize your thoughts and write a fun, interesting story!

### Key Terms:

Narrative: A text that tells a story

- If it's a <u>true story</u>, that makes it a **nonfiction narrative**
- If it's a <u>made-up or imagined story</u>, that makes it a **fictional narrative**
- Narratives can be either **literary** or **informational** (or sometimes both!), depending on their content

    o If it's a made-up story, it's **literary**
    o If it's a nonfiction narrative that tells the story of history or of a particular person, it's **informational** too!

### Elements of a Narrative

- **CHARACTERS:** The people or human-like animals or objects that interact in the story
    o Usually, there is a <u>main character</u> known as the **protagonist** and an enemy or obstacle known as the **antagonist**

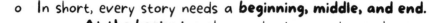
- **PLOT:** The events of the story laid out in a <u>sequence</u>

  o In short, every story needs a **beginning, middle, and end.**
    - <u>**At the beginning**</u> the reader learns about the <u>setting</u> and what the story is about
    - <u>**In the middle**</u>, the protagonist travels, meets new people, and over-comes obstacles
    - **Toward the end,** the protagonist confronts the antagonist and the results directly lead to the end of the story.

- **SETTING:** The time and place in which the story happens

  o A setting can be a real place, somewhere totally made up, or anything in between

<u>Crafting a Narrative</u>

- Like writing a good response, crafting a narrative is all about **planning and thinking!**

  o Don't just start a story **without knowing where you're going!**

  o <u>**Do some brainstorming first**</u> and jot down a few notes about what you want to happen.

- Always make sure it's <u>clear</u> to the reader who the main characters are right away and that you explain those characters' personalities right away

- Show the reader early on why the events in the story are **important**

  o If the reader doesn't care, they probably won't read very closely!

  o If the events of the story feel important, readers will be excited to continue moving through your story!

- Before you get too far in the story, make sure the reader understands the **setting**.

  o If the story seems to take place in the "real world" and then there's suddenly magic or a dragon at the end, that would probably be very confusing!

## "Wal Henderson"

## From *Tales of the Trail*

## By Henry Inman

In one of the busy little mining camps just over the range in New Mexico there prowled around, about twenty-five years ago, a notorious character whose life was made up of desperate adventures, and whose tragic death, which is the subject of this sketch, illustrates the inevitable fate of the average border bully.

Wal Henderson was born and "raised"—as he termed it—in Missouri. He came over the mountains into the New Mexico mines from Colorado soon after the first discovery of gold in the Moreno hills, where he staked off a claim in Humbug Gulch, and commenced working in an apparently honest way. He was a rough fellow who could not read, possessing the body of a giant, courageous as a she-grizzly with cubs, and such a dead shot with his revolver that he soon became a terror to the whole mountain population. He was a desperado in its fullest sense, without one redeeming quality, except that he was kind to his dog, a wicked-looking cur, fit companion for such a surly master.

1. **Circle** the details from the text that help you understand **where** these events took place.

2. According to the passage, why did Wal Henderson move to a new state?

   **A.** He was looking for his long-lost family

   **B.** He was looking for gold

   **C.** He was looking for work

   **D.** He got kicked out of his previous home

3. Which of these words means the same thing as "surly," as it is used in the last sentence of the passage?

   **A.** Mean

   **B.** Kind

   **C.** Happy

   **D.** Sad

4. Based on the passage, what key event **definitely** happens later in the story?

   **A.** Wal's marriage

   **B.** Wal finds gold

   **C.** Wal's death

   **D.** Wal fighting a bear

5. In this passage, the author describes someone who is very tough and unpleasant. On the lines below, write **a 2-3 sentence description** of someone who is exactly the **opposite**. Try to describe what qualities make someone **nice** and **gentle**, unlike Wal.

_____

_____

_____

_____

_____

_____

## Planning & Brainstorming a Story

**Directions:** This week, you'll be coming up with a **story** of your own! Take a few minutes to think about what kind of story you'd like to tell! It could be realistic, fantasy, or any other kind of story that you enjoy! After you've had some time to brainstorm, fill out the sheet below to help you think about your **setting, characters, and plot!**

### 1. SETTING:

In the box below, brainstorm **some different words** that describe the kind of place where your story happens. Is it like the normal world? Is it magical? Does the story mostly happen indoors or outdoors? What is special about this place? Don't feel like you have to write in sentences!

### 2. CHARACTERS:

In the two boxes, below, describe **two** characters (one per box). Put their names at the top of the boxes, then write down some words that describe each character: What do they look like? What is their personality like? What makes them bad, good, or special?

NAME:_____

NAME:_____

3. **PLOT SUMMARY:**

On the lines below, write a **one-sentence** summary of what will happen in your story. Don't feel like you need to be too specific, just provide a general idea of what happens!

_____

_____

_____

_____

_____

_____

## FITNESS

Please be aware of your environment and be safe at all times. If you cannot do an exercise, just try your best.

Repeat these **exercises 3 ROUNDS**

**1 - Abs:** 3 times

**2 - Lunges:** 2 times to each leg.
Note: Use your body weight or books as weight to do leg lunges.

**3 - Plank:** 6 sec.

**4 - Run:** 50m
Note: Run 25 meters to one side and 25 meters back to the starting position.

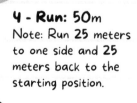

## From "Fifty Years a Detective"

## By Thomas Furlong

Identification of criminals from descriptions is not always an easy task, for two reasons. First, there are but few men who can intelligently describe a person from memory. This is an art within itself. The second reason is, it takes so little to change the general appearance of a man to such a degree that it is hard to pick him up from a mere description, that is, unless the man wanted has some peculiar feature or form that is very noticeable.

The ordinary man, to change his general appearance, has to do but little. A change of shape or style of hat or clothing, the cutting off or growing of a mustache, or even a haircut or shave will often serve the purpose. I have never claimed to have what is today called "a camera eye" but I did a piece of identification work while special agent of the Allegheny Valley Railroad in the early '70s of which I have always been proud, for the reason that there has absolutely never been another case like it in the police history of the entire country.

1. **Underline** the **two reasons** the author says descriptions of criminals are difficult.

2. Based on the final sentences of the passage, what do you think would come next after this passage?

_____

_____

3. Based on the passage, which of these was probably the author's job?

   **A.** Doctor
   **B.** Police
   **C.** Firefighter
   **D.** Teacher

4. Based on the passage, which of these phrases means the same thing as "camera eye?" (Paragraph 2)

A. Ability to see into the future

B. Perfect memory

C. Large telescope

D. Artificial eyeball

5. If you were trying to hide your identity like the criminals in the passage, what could you do to change the way you looked? Try to brainstorm at least three ideas!

_____

_____

_____

_____

## Writing Your Story

**Directions:** Using the notes you created on Day 1, write the story you brainstormed on the lines below. Make sure to describe the **setting** of the story, introduce the **characters**, and explain what happens in the **plot!** Your story should be <u>at least</u> five sentences long, but it can be as long as you want!

Use your **imagination** and **have fun** – you've earned it!

# FITNESS

Please be aware of your environment and be safe at all times. If you cannot do an exercise, just try your best.

Repeat these **exercises 3 ROUNDS**

**2 - Side Bending:** 5 times to each side. Note: try to touch your feet.

**3 - Tree Pose:** Stay as long as possible. Note: do the same with the other leg.

**1 - Squats:** 5 times.
Note: imagine you are trying to sit on a chair.

# MATH

**WEEK 12 DAY 3** **WINTER**

1. Which clock shows 9:15?

1    2    3    4

A. 1
B. 2
C. 3
D. 4

2. Look at the analog clock:

Which digital clock shows the same time?

| 1:30 | 6:10 | 5:10 | 2:30 |

1     2     3     4

A. 1
B. 2
C. 3
D. 4

3. How much money is there in the picture?

A. 55 ¢
B. 66 ¢
C. 91 ¢
D. $ 1.06

4. Subtract 71 ¢ from $3.

A. $ 2 and 24 ¢
B. $ 2 and 26 ¢
C. $ 2 and 29 ¢
D. $ 1 and 34 ¢

5. What is the difference between $136 and $42?

6. Which shape shows the fraction $\frac{5}{9}$?

1     2     3     4

7. What fraction of the shape is unshaded?

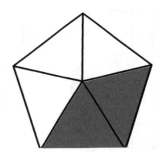

A. $\frac{1}{3}$        C. $\frac{2}{5}$

B. $\frac{3}{5}$        D. $\frac{2}{3}$

8. What fraction of the shapes are circles?

A. $\frac{5}{11}$     C. $\frac{11}{5}$

B. $\frac{11}{15}$     D. $\frac{1}{3}$

9. Where is the point on the number line?

A. $\frac{5}{9}$     C. $\frac{5}{8}$

B. $\frac{3}{8}$     D. $\frac{3}{9}$

10. What fraction does the letter K represent on the number line?

11. Which fraction is represented by the star on the number line?

A. $\frac{1}{6}$ or one-sixth

B. $\frac{2}{6}$ or two-sixths

C. $\frac{4}{8}$ or four-eighths

D. $\frac{3}{8}$ or three-eighths

# FITNESS

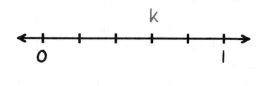

Please be aware of your environment and be safe at all times. If you cannot do an exercise, just try your best.

Repeat these **exercises 3 ROUNDS**

**1 - Bend forward:** 10 times.
Note: try to touch your feet. Make sure to keep your back straight and if needed you can bend your knees.

**2 - Lunges:** 3 times to each leg.
Note: Use your body weight or books as weight to do leg lunges.

**3 - Plank:** 6 sec.

**4 - Abs:**
10 times

1. Which fraction is NOT equivalent to $\frac{1}{2}$?

   A. $\frac{3}{6}$

   B. $\frac{2}{4}$

   C. $\frac{5}{6}$

   D. $\frac{5}{10}$

2. Use a comparison symbol to compare the two fractions below.

   $$\frac{3}{8} \quad\quad \frac{2}{3}$$

3. Are the fractions $\frac{6}{12}$ and $\frac{2}{4}$ equivalent fractions? Explain how you know.

4. Write the fraction $\frac{4}{12}$ in lowest terms.

5. Which rule describes the pattern: 3, 8, 13, 18?

   A. + 2
   B. + 3
   C. + 4
   D. + 5

6. The number pattern is "times 2". Which number is after 6, 12, 24 ?

   A. 30
   B. 36
   C. 48
   D. 72

7. The rule for the pattern shown below is "- 8". Fill in the missing numbers.

   80, 72, _____, 56, _____, 40

8. Start at the number 21 and create a pattern with the rule 'add 7'. What is the fourth number in the pattern?

9. The temperature inside a house was 21°C, which was 5°C warmer than the temperature outside. What temperature was it outside?

10. Dan finished doing his homework at 6:15 p.m. If he had started working on it at 5:25 p.m., how long did it take him to do his homework?

    A. 50 minutes
    B. 1 hour and 50 minutes
    C. 1 hours and 10 minutes
    D. 1 hours and 15 minutes

11. Three feet of ribbon are needed for wrapping each present. How many presents can be wrapped with 72 feet of ribbon?

    A. 16
    B. 20
    C. 24
    D. 36

12. Can you draw a line of symmetry for the figure below? If so, draw all the lines that will make this figure symmetrical.

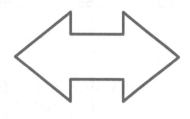

~~~~~~~~~~~~~~~~~~~~

13. Which time would be one hour ahead of the time represented on the clock below?

A. 7:32          C. 6:37
B. 9:32          D. 7:37

14. Which time is represented by 3:45 pm?

A. thirty-four five in the afternoon
B. thirty-four five in the morning
C. three forty-five in the morning
D. three forty-five in the afternoon

15. What time is represented by half past eleven in the morning?

A. 11:30 am
B. 12:30 am
C. 11:30 pm
D. 12:30 pm

# FITNESS

Please be aware of your environment and be safe at all times. If you cannot do an exercise, just try your best.

Repeat these
**exercises**
**3 ROUNDS**

**2 - Chair:** 10 sec.
Note: sit on an imaginary chair, keep your back straight.

**1 - High Plank:**
6 sec.

**3 - Waist Hooping:** 10 times. Note: if you do not have a hoop, pretend you have an imaginary hoop and rotate your hips 10 times.

**4 - Abs:**
10 times

1. If a bucket weighs about **2** kilograms, how many grams does the bucket weigh?

   A. 200 grams
   B. 2,000 grams
   C. 20,000 grams
   D. 20 grams

2. Which number sentence below is true?

   A. $\dfrac{1}{2} = \dfrac{1}{4}$  C. $\dfrac{2}{4} > \dfrac{1}{4}$

   B. $\dfrac{3}{3} < \dfrac{3}{6}$  D. $\dfrac{6}{7} < \dfrac{5}{7}$

3. Which sign makes the statement $\dfrac{2}{5} \,?\, \dfrac{3}{10}$ true?

   A. <
   B. >
   C. =

4. Which time is shown on the clock?

   A. 1 minute after 11
   B. 5 minutes after 11
   C. 11 minutes before 1
   D. 11 minutes before 5

5. Which shows the total amount of **5** pennies?

   A. 1 ¢  C. 5 ¢
   B. 4 ¢  D. 14 ¢

Use the line plot for questions 6-10.
The lengths of some leaves were measured. The line plot shows the number of leaves for each measurement.

Number of Leaves for Each Length

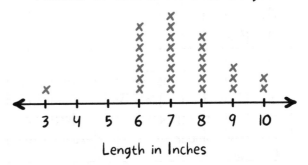

Length in Inches

6. How many leaves measured **6** inches in length?

   A. 6 leaves
   B. 7 leaves
   C. 8 leaves
   D. 9 leaves

7. How many leaves measured **5** inches in length?

   A. 0 leaves
   B. 1 leaves
   C. 3 leaves
   D. 6 leaves

8. There are **3** leaves with the same measurement. How many inches in length does one of those leaves measure?

   A. 3 inches
   B. 6 inches
   C. 8 inches
   D. 9 inches

249

9. One more leaf was measured and added to the line plot. The leaf measured 8 inches. Which shows the new number of leaves that measured 8 inches?

   A. 5 leaves
   B. 6 leaves
   C. 7 leaves
   D. 8 leaves

10. Two more leaves were measured and added to the line plot. Both of the leaves measured 5 inches in length. Which shows the new number of leaves that measured 5 inches?

    A. 0 leaves
    B. I leaves
    C. 2 leaves
    D. 3 leaves

11. Which shape does NOT have 3 sides?

   A.     C.

   B.     D.

12. Which shape has equal parts?

   A.     C.

   B.     D.

 YOGA

Please be aware of your environment and be safe at all times. If you cannot do an exercise, just try your best.

**1 - Down Dog:** 10 sec.

**2 - Bend Down:** 10 sec.

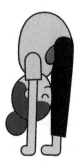

**3 - Chair:** 10 sec.

**4 - Child Pose:** 20 sec.

**5 - Shavasana:** as long as you can. Note: think of happy moments and relax your mind.

## Simulating a Volcano

So far, we've looked at **erosion** and **earthquakes** as examples of natural forces that can be extremely destructive. Today, we'll round out our summer by looking at another kind of natural disaster, while also completing one of the most famous science experiments of all time. It's time to create a **volcano**!

Volcanos are spots where magma from the Earth's extremely hot inner layers can burst out onto the surface as lava. Lava can be as hot as 1,600 degrees, which means that it can burn or destroy just about anything in its path. Today we'll recreate that lava flow without the crazy temperatures!

### Materials:

- A safe outdoor area to experiment
- A plastic cup or water bottle
- 4 tablespoons of Baking Soda
- 1 cup of Vinegar
- A few drops of red food coloring
- 1 spoon
- A few small toys or action figures (optional)

### Procedure:

1. Bring your plastic cup or water bottle outside and build a mound of dirt around it so it looks like the top of the bottle or cup is the opening at the top of a volcano.

2. If you brought any small toys or action figures with you, you can set them up at the base of your mountain of dirt or the nearby area. These will represent people, buildings, cars, and other objects that might be near the volcano.

3. Put the 4 tablespoons of baking soda inside your cup or bottle.

4. In another cup or glass, mix the food coloring into the vinegar and stir to mix.

5. Pour the cup of vinegar into the bottle and observe what happens (there may be a slight delay - if the delay feels long, try to give the mixture a quick stir).

6. Observe what happens as the "lava" flows out of the volcano and toward any toys or other objects you set up nearby. Imagine what it would be like if it was actually 1,600 degrees!

7. You can repeat this experiment 1 or 2 times, if you want, before your volcano loses its shape.

8. Clean up your materials (watch out - there may be a strong vinegar smell!) and answer the questions below.

**Follow-Up Questions:**

1.  Describe what you saw when you mixed the baking soda and vinegar:

_____

_____

_____

2.  How would your results have been different if the "lava" from your volcano was actually 1,600 degrees?

_____

_____

_____

 YOGA

Please be aware of your environment and be safe at all times. If you cannot do an exercise, just try your best.

**1 - Tree Pose:** Stay as long as possible. Note: do on one leg then on another.

**2 - Down Dog:** 10 sec.

**3 - Stretching:** Stay as long as possible. Note: do on one leg then on another.

**5 - Book Pose:** 6 sec. Note: Keep your core tight. Legs should be across from your eyes.

**6 - Shavasana:** 5 min. Note: this pose is very important and provides you with long term benefits. Try not to skip this. Close your eyes and imagine who you want to be and what your goals are! Always think happy thoughts.

**4 - Lower Plank:** 6 sec. Note: Keep your back straight and body tight.

**Task:** There are seven houses connected to a different object. Color in each path (using a different color) to locate which object belongs to which house.

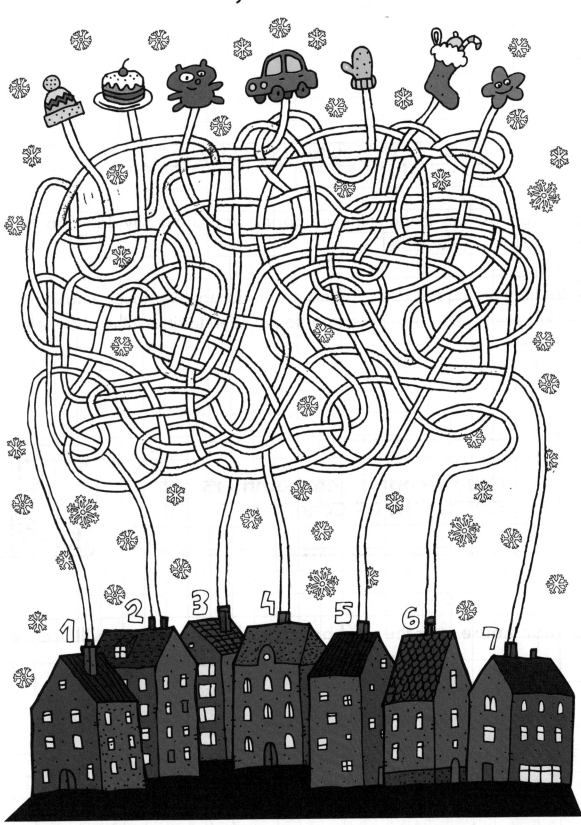

# Answer Sheets

To see the answer key to the entire workbook, you can easily download the answer key from our website!

*Due to the high request from parents and teachers, we have removed the answer key from the workbook so you do not need to rip out the answer key while students work on the workbook.

 Go to **argoprep.com/summer3**
OR scan the QR Code:

**Place your mouse over the workbook you have, and you will see the "Download Answers" button.**

Kids Summer Academy by ArgoPrep: Grade 8-9

Kids Summer Academy by ArgoPrep: Grade 5-6

Kids Summer Academy by ArgoPrep: Grade 4-5

Kids Summer Academy by ArgoPrep: Grade 6-7

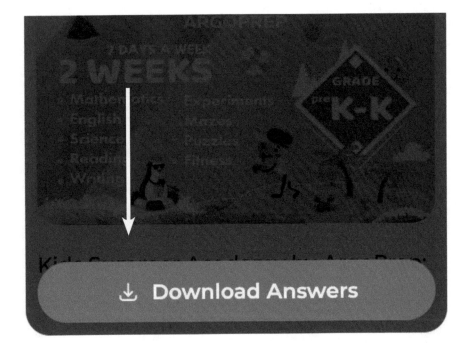

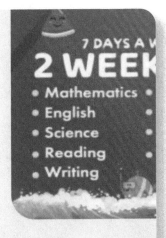

Kids Summer
Grade 8-9